THE MYSTERY OF GHOSTLY VERA
And Other Haunting Tales of Southwest Virginia

Charles Edwin Price

Introduction by Sharyn McCrumb

Cover Art by David Dixon

The Overmountain Press

JOHNSON CITY, TENNESSEE

Other books by Charles Edwin Price

Haints, Witches and Boogers:
Tales From Upper East Tennessee

Demon in the Woods:
Tall Tales and True From East Tennessee

The Day They Hung The Elephant

ISBN 0-932807-88-7

1 2 3 4 5 6 7 8 9 0

Contents

Acknowledgments

I want to thank the following people who helped me and were responsible for many of the stories in this book and who provided encouragement throughout the writing.

First of all, I would like to thank L.C. Angle, President of the Washington County Historical Society, for his conversation and his providing valuable background on Washington County history. To use a hackneyed, but very apt expression, L.C. is a true gentleman and scholar.

Secondly, I'd like to express my appreciation to Gary and Marie Frank, owners of Main Street Books in Abingdon, for suggesting I write such a volume in the first place. I sincerely hope that the result pleases them.

Thanks to Martha Weisfeld of the *Abingdon Virginian*, a truly remarkable woman, for telling me the story of "Wood" Lyon.

Thanks to my good friend at Virginia Intermont College, Elaine Lang, for providing the chilling tales of her house near Bristol and the experience with the ghost of her grandfather in Blue Ridge.

Also I'd like to offer sincere appreciation to Debbie Bourne, Jan Durbin, Pete Sheffey, Melody Bowers, and all the staff at the Martha Washington Inn for helping me piece together a reasonable account of the ghostly happenings at the Inn.

Thanks to the administration at Virginia Intermont College, especially Jeff Prince, in providing material on the ghost of "Vera." It was through their efforts, as well as alumnus Martha Brown, that the mystery of the ghost has been—at least partially—solved. A special thanks to John Tallman for introducing me to the legend of "Vera" in the first place, and to Jamie Smith for providing an account of her experiences with the ghost.

Also much thanks to John and Maureen Stanton of Knoxville, Keith Snodgrass and Michelle Jones of Mountain Empire Community College in Big Stone Gap, Sarah Zimmerman and Ed Moorer of The New River Historical Society, Sondra Blevins and Tina Jennings of Cave House, and Rex Partington and Pearl Hayter of the Barter Theatre for their help and encouragement.

Last, but certainly not least, to Judy Blevins and Sherry Lewis at The Overmountain Press, for their brave efforts to straighten out my flawed prose.

Thanks, too, to master mystery author Sharyn McCrumb for doing me the honor of writing the introduction for this book.

And to everyone else who gave me help and encouragement during this project....

For Anne LeCroy

Introduction

"They brought their fiddle tunes from Ireland, their knowledge of whiskey-making from Scotland, and their quilt patterns from a time before history began." Thus I described the pinions of Southern mountain culture in my Appalachian novel **The Hangman's Beautiful Daughter**. I might also have added that these pioneering hillfolk brought with them not only quilt patterns, but story patterns as well.

Stories have a shape. Like verbal quilt patterns, the configurations of these oral art works have a sameness to them, regardless of the national fabric or local color that alters the details with each retelling. Just as a bear-claw quilt is a recognizable form, whether it is fashioned in red cotton on white or polyester green on blue, so the *sagen*, as the folklorists call them, keep their pattern through many varieties of tellings, even when the "*Wexford* Girl" becomes the "*Knoxville* Girl."

We have all learned the story-shapes, from our childhood tales, our earliest introduction into western culture: it is the *third* bowl of porridge or chair or bed that Goldilocks will choose; it is the youngest son, who is left the worthless memento of his father, who will prosper; and it is the poor, but kindly soul who will be rescued by supernatural intervention, *a la Cinderella*. Perhaps now we have so thoroughly shaped stories that they have begun to shape us, so that we remember tales the way they ought to have happened. Perhaps this is why ghosts are beautiful young girls, star-crossed in love (*Ghosts of Martha Washington*), rather than prune-faced old biddies with nothing better to do in the Hereafter. It is why witches always have *black* animals for pets (*The Black Dog of Coeburn*), never a nice Irish setter or a ginger cat. And the Civil War dead keep fighting the same battle over and over (*An Army of Ghosts*), while the living veterans put the war behind them: soldiers from both sides reminisced together at Gettysburg reunions, and Confederate General Joseph Johnston served as a pallbearer at the funeral of William T. Sherman. Conditioned by millennia of stories in our blood, we think that sad ghosts ought to be pretty, and the tragedy of war never ends.

My Blue Ridge Mountain home, southwest Virginia, abounds with legends. It has been said that in Virginia the ghosts outnumber the people. In **The Mystery of Ghostly Vera and Other Haunting Tales of**

Southwest Virginia, folklore collector Charles Edwin Price has assembled a sampling of the phantom citizenry of the region, preserving these stories just as they have been handed down by generations of folk in the Blue Ridge. It is as rich a heritage as the coal seams that lace the hollers of Appalachia. Aristotle said: "The friend of myth is also a friend of wisdom." We can learn much from these tales of supernatural occurrences in the southern mountain: the legends can trace storytelling patterns back to ancient cultures in Europe, illuminate the unconscious fears of the frontier dweller, and give us new insights into the history of the region.

But first the stories must be collected and preserved. We are in Ed's debt for his efforts at saving a precious legacy: our oral history.

Sharyn McCrumb
Shawsville, Virginia

About the Tales

—A hideous ghost with half a head that confronts nocturnal travelers near Snowville.

—A house that may be haunted by not one, but a whole family of ghosts.

—A world-famous theater haunted by the spirit of the man who founded it.

—A riderless horse seen roaming the grounds of the Martha Washington Inn, and the spritely, violin-playing apparition of a "white lady" within.

—A mysterious ghost of a tragic young woman said to haunt the halls of Virginia Intermont College in Bristol.

—A ghost with a treasure, who forever hides the gold from the grasp of the living.

—The horrifying account of a mysterious resident of Big Stone Gap who was rumored to be a vampire or, at the very least, a terrifying cannibal.

—The ghost of a child in Wise who is easily upset when someone in her house argues with another person.

—A monstrous black dog who haunts a remote hollow near Coeburn.

—Three sinister sisters in Christiansburg who dealt in fraud, witchcraft, and murder.

These are a few of the hauntings and other strange enigmatic tales that abound in and around Abingdon, Bristol, Wise, Big Stone Gap, Coeburn, Saltville, and throughout the rest of Southwest Virginia.

The area abounds in tales of the supernatural. Indeed, nearly everyone I met on my collecting trips had a story of some sort or the other—either personal or secondhand—to tell. And, of course, each story was declared by its teller to be absolutely true.

Ghostly tales have existed for hundreds of years. Some date back to the 1700s, when the land was first settled by pioneers crossing rugged mountains or traveling down the beautiful Shenandoah Valley from Maryland or Pennsylvania.

For a long time, until the coming of the railroads, these were people isolated by the Appalachian Mountains. Even today, some of the terrain of Southwest Virginia is difficult to negotiate—even in modern motor vehicles. (Anyone who has had the misfortune to travel from Marion to Tazewell over State Route 16 knows exactly what I mean.) Imagine what it might have been like in the 1700s when the first pioneers traversed those incredible mountains in horse-drawn vehicles or afoot!

But traverse the mountains, they did. Towns sprung up, and the seeds of civilization settled over the land. But as settlement progressed, strife broke out and wars rent Southwest Virginia. Battles raged and people died violent deaths.

First came the Cherokee Indians who fought against encroachment of the whites. Then came the Revolution—then The War Between The States. With each succeeding generation came new challenges, new solutions, and new victories. And through it all, the people of Southwest Virginia kept their ethic of hard work and their good sense of humor.

The first settlers of Southwest Virginia were an ethnic mix of nationalities—French, German, Scot, English, Irish—thrown together in the common quest of a new start in life. Each group had its own folklore, brought with them in their journeys from the Old World. In time, the various traditions combined, and a new "Appalachian folklore" emerged, much of which consisted of ghost and witch lore.

Storytelling was an entertainment on the frontier. Settlers gathered around the warm hearths of log cabins, on cold winter evenings, and told tales of adventure and heroism—and ghosts.

The new Appalachian lore was steeped in history because the region was so important in the political and economic development of the new country called America. A number of towns in Southwest Virginia evolved as important centers of this development. One of these was the little village of Abingdon.

Located in extreme Southwest Virginia's rugged mountains, Abingdon is well over 200 years old. Daniel Boone first named it "Wolf Hill" because of the pack of wolves that lived in a cave behind the present Cave House Craft Shop. The wolves harassed Boone's dogs during a hunting trip in 1760.

The first settlers built homes on Wolf Hill around 1768. Dr. Thomas Walker donated 120 acres on which to build the town. Then he subdivided it into lots and sold homesites to settlers.

The next name given to Abingdon was "Black's Fort," in honor of fortifications built there in 1776. In 1778, Black's Fort was renamed

Abingdon.

The first post office in Southwest Virginia was established in Abingdon in 1793, and the town was a distributing point for mail and supplies to settlements in the west.

Abingdon, as historian Walter H. Hendricks wrote, was one of the "seedbeds of our nation." A Virginia governor wrote, after The War Between The States, "...no other town of similar size in America gave as many distinguished sons to the South and the nation as Abingdon."

Three Virginia governors came from Abingdon, or the immediate vicinity: Wyndham Robertson, David Campbell, and John B. Floyd, Jr. Other statesmen and jurists included U.S. Senator John W. Johnston, Secretary of the Treasury John Campbell, Secretary of War John B. Floyd, and Chief Justice of the Supreme Court of Virginia Preston W. Campbell.

Today, the tourist trade constitutes a large part of Abingdon's economy. Yet the town is self-sufficient unto itself. There is industry here, and large retail and service chains operate stores in Abingdon.

But most of all, Abingdon has a distinct personality, unlike that of many Disneyland-type towns that depend on tourists for their daily bread.

L.C. Angle is a retired engineer with Appalachian Power. He is also a retired colonel in the United States Army. Presently, Angle is president of the Washington County Historical Society. He has lived the past 35 years in Abingdon.

"The friendliness of the people is what sets Abingdon apart from anywhere else," Angle said recently. "Above all, the town is genuine."

Perhaps the same can be said for Abingdon's ghosts. While some encounters have been frightening, the ghosts of Abingdon enjoy a certain kinship with the living. The memory of the many ghosts seen in the Martha Washington Inn, for example, is lovingly perpetuated by those who work there day after day. Ghost tours are regularly conducted through the rambling old inn by long-time employee Pete Sheffey.

Too, the ghosts of the Barter Theatre are no strangers to Abingdon. One is instantly recognizable and is an intrinsic part of that operation. The magic ambiance surrounding the world-famous Barter Theatre would suffer greatly from his loss.

And there are many, many other tales.

For thousands of years, mankind has believed in ghosts. From the ancient Egyptians and Babylonians, through the spiritualist movement of the nineteenth century, to modern day, people have wanted to believe in a life after death. That is why they have held to their belief in ghosts and the supernatural.

As I said earlier, the folklore of Southwest Virginia is filled with such stories. Belief in ghosts transcends all classes of people, every level of economic and intellectual condition. The ghosts of Abingdon—indeed, in all of Southwest Virginia—are permanent fixtures in the mind of a people, not only mindful of their rich heritage, but of their extraordinary place in the history of the United States.

Their ghosts are constant reminders of that past.

Charles Edwin Price
Winter 1993

The Ghostly Tavern

Every once in a while, on very dark, still nights, a red glow can be seen through a second story window of the old tavern on Main Street in Abingdon. The light appears to come from a single source, moves slowly from side to side, disappears, then reappears again.

At other times, when no one is in the building, a nerve-shattering shriek is heard from within—the unmistakable sound of a woman screaming in terror for her life. It's the kind of sound a person doesn't forget very easily and raises the hackles on the back of the neck.

Swarthy shadows in the darkened tavern appear alive with the otherworld. Some say one of the tavern's ghosts is the lost soul of a man murdered in a card game—the other is the terrified spirit of a woman murdered in cold blood by an inhuman monster.

Whatever the genesis of the ghost(s), few can deny that spirits of some sort dwell in the antediluvian building—often claimed to be the oldest existing structure in Abingdon. The tavern may have been raised as early as 1788 by John Campbell.

Campbell was born in Augusta County and arrived in the vicinity of Marion in 1765. There he purchased a tract of land on the Middle Fork of the Holston River, calling it "Royal Oak." Later, he purchased land in the southern end of Washington County which was known as Hall's Bottom.

John Campbell and his family distinguished themselves in public service. His son, Colonel John Campbell, became Treasurer of the United States under President Andrew Jackson. A grandson, David, was Governor of Virginia from 1837-1841. Another grandson, William B., was Governor of Tennessee; and a brother-in-law, Archibald Roane, was also a Tennessee governor (1801-1804), succeeding John Sevier.

Southwest Virginia was a vast wilderness in 1788, populated by hordes of wild animals, and was the principal hunting ground of Cherokee Indians. Indeed, the Cherokee had invaded Southwest Virginia, East Tennessee and Western North Carolina sometime in the fourteenth century. After defeating incumbent tribes, the Cherokee founded their permanent villages, mainly located on the Little Tennessee River. Most of their other conquered land, including Northeast Tennessee and Southwest Virginia, was used by the Cherokees primarily as hunting grounds.

No roads crossed Virginia's tangled thickets and verdant hillsides. Those who chose to make homes in the wilderness made do with narrow paths cut through the rugged terrain by wandering herds of animals or by Indian hunting parties. But civilization was poised, ready to enter the untamed frontier on the backs of the first people to settle there. The days of the Indian were numbered, though they fought valiantly for years in an attempt to retain their territory.

But civilization *did* finally come. Population increased; more and more settlers moved in. The Indians continued to wage war but, in the long run, the effort was star-crossed. The whites were there to stay.

On December 6, 1776, Fincastle County was divided into thirds. The southernmost tract was called Washington County, named in honor of the Revolutionary War general and, later, first President of the United States.

From the beginning, the county seat of Washington County was Abingdon (called then, Black's Fort). In those days, Abingdon was a trading center—a gateway to the West. Like later cattle towns in the "Wild West," Abingdon was a stopping off place for road-weary drovers looking for fun and relaxation.

David Campbell, later Governor of Virginia, said that when he first saw Black's Fort in 1788, it consisted of four log cabins—three of which were taverns. Obviously it was a two-fisted settlement in those early days. That same year, the name of the town was changed to Abingdon by an act of the General Assembly of Virginia.

By 1793, the first Post Office on either the Holston or Clinch River was established at Abingdon, with Gerrard T. Conn as postmaster.

Abingdon was becoming respectable—at least on the surface.

But there was still an element of lawlessness in the town. Abingdon taverns were dens of iniquity, and the famous tavern was probably no exception. Games of chance started at the drop of a hat. Combined with strong drink and lax law enforcement, an innocent card game could quickly turn into an excuse for murder.

One night, in the early part of the nineteenth century, a weary drover visited the tavern in search of liquid refreshment and divertissement. Eventually he got into a card game which continued far into the night.

The drover was lucky at cards, winning most of his opponents' money. His companions turned surly. He was accused of cheating. No man could have that much luck at cards without having an ace tucked up his sleeve.

No amount of explanation quelled the rage of his cronies, who slew him in cold blood in an alley outside the tavern. The murderers escaped, but the murdered man's soul was imprisoned in the tavern where it has been both seen and heard ever since.

Could this man's spirit be the source of the ghost light seen in the tavern windows? Perhaps. But the light could also represent a second spirit said to lurk inside the aging tavern.

A second tale concerns a ribald lass who unabashedly sold her favors to all comers. Then, as now, this was a dangerous profession, and one night the young lady in question came to a violent end in the clutches of a merciless fiend.

The evening began reasonably enough when a group of weary mule skinners stopped in Abingdon for the night. Naturally the fellowship gravitated to the tavern, their throats dry after many miles on the rough, dusty trail.

One of the mule skinners we'll call Pete. Pete was a mountain of a man, very strong and muscular, and a hard worker. You could also say that Pete was lacking in the most elemental of social graces. In fact, he was well-known for his cruelty towards both man and beast. When our barmaid approached Pete that night, she had no idea what she was getting herself into.

At first, the pairing was quite amiable. In fact, both were in the process of getting happily soused on a local vintage and were soon feeling no pain. Then the girl suggested that she and Pete retire to the second floor.

Fifteen minutes later, the girl's anguished screams echoed throughout the tavern. Men coming to her rescue found her battered, bleeding body sprawled on the floor of one of the upstairs rooms. (Of the five rooms now upstairs in The Tavern, the consensus of opinion is that she was murdered in the back room on the right.)

"Who did this?" one of the men asked.

Breathing her last, the girl identified Pete as her murderer. When the men searched the tavern for Pete, he was gone.

The sheriff questioned Pete's fellow drovers. No, they had not seen him. The town and surrounding countryside were searched. Nothing. Pete had disappeared from the face of the earth and was never seen again in Abingdon.

For more than 100 years, the haunted tavern building was owned by Thaddeus and Mary Jane Harris and their descendants. Harris was a barber and hairdresser who worked at The Washington House, the hotel next door. Built by Thomas Findlay in 1835, The Washington House was the first regular hotel to be built in Abingdon.

In the early part of 1861, after South Carolina, Mississippi, Florida, Alabama, and Georgia voted for secession from the Union, a crowd of townspeople, angered that the rest of Washington County had over-whelmingly voted against secession (2930 against vs 1151 for), strung a rope across Main Street near the tavern. There they hung a Confederate flag and proceeded to hold a rally. Thaddeus Harris must have been alarmed at the sight, because he was a free Negro and feelings about blacks were already getting a bit tense in the town.

A month before, the Washington County Court, attempting to head off possible racial trouble, had ordered all "free persons of color" to leave the county. Harris and three other blacks of property (Samuel Merchant, Barbary Beverly and Senah Richmond), however, were given permission to remain in town for 90 days "for the purpose of settling their business." An unruly, agitated mob, determined to hoist the Confederate flag against popular opinion, was the last thing Harris wanted to see at the time.

Anti-secessionists were also alarmed at the impromptu rally. William B. Clark, in particular, was incensed. "That damned rag!" he shouted as he saw the flag hanging from the rope in the middle of Main Street. "Boys, it is not the flag of our fathers." Then without further ado, the anti-secessionists attacked the rope, tore down the "stars and bars," and burned it.

Victory was fleeting, however. War was imminent and the secessionists would eventually win out. Virginia, itself, was preparing to pull away from the Union. On April 17, 1861, Virginia adopted an ordinance that repealed ratification of the U.S. Constitution by the state. The die was cast.

Oddly enough, those most opposed to the hoisting of the Confederate standard in Abingdon were among the first to volunteer service in the Army of Virginia. William Clark, himself, joined the 37th Virginia Infantry and died in battle.

Four years later, April 9, 1865, Lee surrendered his army to General Grant at Appomattox Courthouse in Virginia. And on that date, Thaddeus Harris still lived with his family in Abingdon. His 90 days grace had expired, but he was not required to leave town. One explanation may have been that he had found a white man of "good standing" to stand security for his good behavior.

Mary Dudley Porterfield, wife of Barter Theatre founder Robert Porterfield, bought the property from the Harris family in 1964.

During its existence, the tavern building served as a tavern, bank, bakery, cabinet shop, barber shop, private residence, post office, and antique shop. The building has been restored and presently houses a fine restaurant.

Today, The Tavern speaks loudly of its age. The ground floor consists of brick underfoot. The well-worn stairs leading to the second floor list to starboard from heavy use.

On the second floor, the visitor sees wide-board ceilings, gas-fed fireplaces, plaster walls, wide-board hardwood floors, woodwork painted antique gray, door jambs that sag to one side, old-fashioned door locks and latches, and even cracks in the ceiling.

But age is arbitrary when a person speaks of the old tavern. When first built, the building smelled of fresh-cut wood and linseed oil. At that time the hearth wasn't stained with soot. The structure, in that respect, is ageless—just like its ghosts.

The ghosts of The Tavern are seen and heard often. The ghost light is best observed on dark mornings, between 1:00 and 2:00 a.m., the approximate time that the card-playing drover was murdered by his cronies. The screams of the unfortunate barmaid can be heard anytime.

When I spoke to the present manager of The Tavern recently, he denied he's heard any ghostly goings-on in the building. But I've interviewed two town residents who swear they, personally, have seen the ghost light. Another has heard the screams—on at least three occasions.

Legends die hard. The Tavern is steeped in generations of history. Considering all that had gone on before, to believe that shadows of the past may have missed an opportunity to haunt the old structure would be considered unthinkable.

The Ghosts of the Martha Washington Inn

Guests who occupy Room 403 at the Martha Washington Inn may get more than a place to sleep for the night. They may get a chilling glimpse into the supernatural!

Room 403 is the home of a ghost affectionately known as "Beth." Her misty apparition has been seen—and her noisy shenanigans heard—by both staff and guests.

One night a woman and her husband were staying in Room 403. Before retiring, the couple flipped on the TV. As they watched, the brass bed on which they were sitting began to shake violently.

"I thought there was an earthquake," the woman said. Startled, the couple ran across the room and out the door.

Another time a night clerk heard the heavy footfalls of a guest running down the grand staircase in the middle of the night. Without a word, the agitated guest threw his room keys on the desk, turned, and ran through the door in such haste that his baggage caught in the doorway. After a short struggle, the guest untangled his luggage, ran off the porch, and fled across the lawn into the night.

"He must have seen or heard something, but he didn't say what," the puzzled night clerk said. "He was a regular guest and had stayed at The Inn many times before. But this was the first time I've ever seen him behave like that."

Had the guest seen the apparition of the heartbroken Beth standing by his bedside? Or did he see one of the other ghosts which are said to haunt The Martha Washington Inn? Could it have been the wounded Confederate soldier? Or could the guest have peered out his window to see the phantom riderless horse roaming the grounds? Maybe the tortured ghost of a black slave, said to haunt The Pub, visited him in the middle of the night. How about the ghost of a former waiter, Luther Price, which bellman Pete Sheffey thinks may haunt the cavernous building?

No one knows for sure how many ghosts haunt the Martha Washington Inn. One? Two? Three? More? Those with personal experiences report both apparitions and poltergeist activity—a great deal of it—mainly in the winter. During research for this book, I spoke to a number of Martha Washington Inn employees about their experiences.

(These interviews, I might add, were made on company time with the complete cooperation of management. I get the distinct feeling the owners of The Martha Washington Inn consider their ghosts an asset. And come to think of it, why not? Sleeping in a haunted house appeals to many people's sense of adventure.)

The Martha Washington Inn speaks loudly of its age and elegance. Polished wooden floors creak when walked upon. Ceilings are high, remaining so even after renovation of the building in 1984. A huge curving staircase ascends grandly from the foyer to the top floor. Crystal chandeliers hang in all the main rooms. Rich paintings adorn the walls. Fireplaces abound.

The oldest building (the one in the center) was built in 1832 as a home by General Francis Preston. Born in Greenfield in 1765, he was a son of Colonel William Preston (1730-1783). After graduation from William and Mary College, Preston returned to Abingdon and set up his law practice.

He served as a Virginia Congressman from 1793 to 1797, the result of a hotly contested election. Preston, a Washingtonian Federalist, ran against Abraham Trigg, a Jeffersonian Democrat. Preston won the election by ten votes and Trigg cried "foul." Trigg swore the election was rigged and that Preston was not only in cahoots with both the sheriffs of Washington and Lee Counties, but that Preston's brother, William, had intimidated voters by marching 60 or 70 Federal troops through the Montgomery Courthouse. Trigg further alleged that Captain William Preston had stationed some of his troops in the doorway of the courthouse, refusing admission to supporters of Trigg.

The dispute moved to the halls of Congress itself, where various factions squabbled for days. Finally, the Elections Committee of the House of Representatives recommended the unseating of Preston. But a House vote rejected the recommendation, and Preston was allowed to serve.

(Trigg finally did make it to Congress, but only after Preston was unseated in 1797. Trigg served with distinction from that date until 1809.)

Francis Preston was one of the first slaveholders in Washington County to emancipate a slave. On September 20, 1795, Preston deeded John Broady, a former slave to General William Campbell, his freedom.

Broady claimed the General promised him freedom. Preston had married Campbell's daughter, Sarah Buchanan Campbell, and Broady came along as part of the marriage settlement. In his deed, Preston said he felt a "desire to emancipate the said negro man John, as well for the fulfillment of the above-mentioned promise, as the gratification of being instrumental of prompting a participation of liberty to a fellow creature, who by nature is entitled thereto...."

Later, Preston served in the War of 1812, first as a Captain in the Seventieth Brigade and later as Major. In 1820, Preston was elected Brigadier General of the Virginia Militia. He also served as a member of the Virginia General Assembly.

At the time Preston built his home, he was a member of the Washington County Court. He was described by a contemporary observer as "once tall, now bent with age—head quite white and face ruddy. He speaks mildly and seems to regret that the stern arbitrament of law is necessary to compel to do right towards their fellow creatures."

Does that sound like the same Francis Preston who was supposed to have rigged an election 30 years before? Age must have mellowed the man.

Preston's magnificent home took two years to build and was touted as the most expensive home in the area. It was built in Federalist style with two floors over an English basement. (The third floor was added in 1905.) Unfortunately, Preston didn't live to enjoy his new digs for long. Two years after the house was finished, he died at the home of his brother in South Carolina.

In 1858, the Preston family sold the house and property to the Holston Conference of the United Methodist Church. Two years later, Martha Washington College was opened to educate young ladies, operating until 1919 when it consolidated with nearby Emory and Henry College. The financially strapped institution finally closed during the height of the Great Depression.

Suddenly the once magnificent edifice became tremendously expensive to maintain. For a time, the building served as living quarters for members of the Barter Theatre. Then it was opened as an inn in 1937 by George G. Barnhill, partially restored, and equipped with antiques. Later the building was bought by United Coal Company (now called The United Company) and restored to its current condition.

I think it would be safe to say that the Martha Washington Inn is the most luxurious haunted house in Abingdon.

The ghosts of the Martha Washington Inn could have sprung from any number of traumatic events occurring there over the past 200 years or so. For instance, even before Preston built his magnificent home, the land on which it stood was befouled with blood.

In 1776 parts of the property were covered by a dense chinquapin thicket. Between the thicket and Black's Fort was open land where colonists grew flax.

One day two men and three women were hard at work pulling flax. Frederick Mongle was stationed as a lookout, his keen eyes peeled for marauding Indians.

These were the years when Cherokees were raiding up and down the frontier. Massacres had already taken place in Southwest Virginia, with colonists killed and women and children kidnapped.

At the edge of the flax field, about a dozen Indians crouched in the bushes, slowly easing up on the flax harvesters, awaiting their first chance to spring. Then a war whoop rent the air, and the Indians charged across the field. Mongle was wounded and scalped alive. The rest of the group fled toward the fort, dodging from tree to tree, protecting themselves from a hail of arrows and blowgun darts. The men in the fort, alerted by screams and war whoops, sprung to the rescue, driving off the Indians and saving all concerned. Then poor Mongle, barely alive, was carried to the fort where he died of his injuries. Could the ghost of Frederick Mongle be among that company of ghosts haunting the Martha Washington Inn?

The War Between The States added to the bloodshed in and around the structure. In December 1864, Washington County was nearly drained of able-bodied men. Most had answered the Confederate call to arms. In the meantime, Federal troops under Generals Stoneman, Gillem, and Burbridge—10,000 men—joined forces in Kentucky and began a march on Southwest Virginia.

The people of Abingdon knew the Federal troops were coming. But want and poverty, combined with the drain on available manpower, had sapped them of most of their will to fight.

Meanwhile, General Duke and a scraggly band of Rebels were camped just outside Abingdon. The little resistance offered to the Federal invasion of the town was provided by them.

When the Confederates formed a line at the intersection of Court and Bailey Streets, they were fired upon by Federals who were advancing up Main Street. Quickly demoralized, the Confederates hightailed it back to their camp.

Stoneman then began burning buildings that were used either as storehouses for Confederate supplies or to house Confederate officials. Destroyed were the railroad depot, Hurt's Store, two wagon shops, and the Washington County jail. However, Stoneman refused to set fire to any private dwellings.

With his headquarters at the Fulkerson house on Colonial Road in west Abingdon, Stoneman thought he was in firm control of the town. But the Confederates still lurked in the surrounding countryside, keeping a low profile. The next morning they sent one of their number, disguised in a Yankee uniform, into town to see what was up. At the same time, a Yankee straggler, James Wyatt, arrived in town on horseback.

Wyatt hailed from Abingdon. He had served as an apprentice to Abingdon Town Council member Gabriel Stickley and somewhere along the line had gotten into trouble with the law. He claimed that Noble I. McGinnis, a member of the Washington County Court, had punished him for an offense for which he was not guilty. He announced that he was going to get revenge by firing the town himself.

Dismounting in front of the county courthouse, he handed the reins to a Negro and lumbered inside. Wyatt climbed to the cupola and set it afire. Then he remounted and began firing all the buildings on the south side of Main Street. As the fire rapidly spread to other wooden structures, Wyatt dared anyone to extinguish the flames.

The Confederate spy returned to camp and reported Wyatt's firing of the town, as well as a gathering of Federal troops at Clark's blacksmith shop. Before long, a number of Confederate soldiers galloped down the hill where the Jackson Institute now stands, splitting their forces at Hayes and Slaughter Streets. Wyatt was still sitting on his horse at the corner of Main and Court Streets, his leg draped over the saddle horn, calmly watching flames devour the town.

Two brothers from Holly Springs, Mississippi, John and Samuel Findlay, both wearing partial Union uniforms, barreled up Main Street on their horses, shooting at Wyatt. The surprised arsonist, mistaking his pursuers for Federals, yelled back that they were firing at their own man. But the Findlays continued shooting.

Suddenly Wyatt charged the two men, galloping past them toward the west end of Abingdon. Samuel Findlay wheeled his horse around and gave chase. Findlay's bullet finally caught up with Wyatt at Hayes Street, and Wyatt fell to the ground.

Wyatt's terrified horse continued running, finally ending up on the campus of Martha Washington College. There the riderless horse wandered about for hours. Wyatt was carried into the home of John Floyd, where he died.

Abingdon resident and Washington County historian, L.C. Angle, claims this is the origin of the legend of the "riderless horse" seen roaming the grounds of the Martha Washington Inn on bright moonlit nights. Apparently, the apparition of a horse without a rider has been seen for many years.

Another version of the story, however, has a Federal officer killed by pursuing Confederates, falling off his horse. The animal, badly frightened, continued on until it reached the campus of Martha Washington College, where it has been seen on moonlit nights ever since.

By far, the most active ghost at the Martha Washington Inn is an apparition known to everyone as "Beth." Beth has been both seen and heard by dozens of people—perhaps even hundreds.

Like his grandfather before him, Pete Sheffey works at the Martha Washington Inn. For the past 32 years he has been a bellman. Sheffey speaks of the old house almost reverently. And he believes the Martha

Washington Inn is really haunted—thoroughly haunted. He knows this because he has had personal experiences with the ghost.

It was about 8:00 p.m. one Sunday evening in February. Sheffey was conducting one of his periodic ghost tours with about 30 people in tow. The group ascended the grand staircase to the second floor and arrived at the door leading to the Governor's Suite.

"It was dark inside the suite," Sheffey remembered with a shudder. "I opened the door and reached in to turn on the light. There was a figure standing in the opposite doorway, inside the suite. I thought at first it was a guest standing there. Then the figure vanished. I knew I had seen a ghost."

Sheffey said the figure appeared to be a woman, tall, with hair down to her shoulders. Shaken, he said he didn't enter the room. Rather, he continued the tour.

An hour later, after the tour ended, Sheffey knew that he had to return to the Governor's Suite to turn off the lights. Again he opened the room. The lights were still on—and he saw the apparition again, this time in the front room by the window. Sheffey slammed the door and ran for a security guard. By the time he and the guard returned to the Governor's Suite, the ghost had vanished and the lights were off.

On another occasion, a security guard saw the apparition of a woman standing in the old dining hall early one morning. The doors were usually locked at 2:00 a.m., and the guard naturally thought that someone had been locked in by mistake. Suddenly he saw the lady come toward him and pass right through the closed doors.

For some reason or other, perhaps out of habit, the security guard addressed the apparition. "May I help you, please?" he asked politely. Then he realized what he had said and what he had seen.

Cautiously he followed the ghost and saw it float up the grand staircase and disappear through the solid wooden door of Room 403. Fortunately, the room was unoccupied that night!

When the guard opened the door and walked into the room, he saw the bed was mussed up, the window blinds were going up and down, and the lights were flicking on and off.

Then there was the time that Kate Trent, a housekeeper, was working in The Pub. She was bent over, vacuuming, when a mist suddenly appeared in front of her. It looked like a woman in white. Then it disappeared.

According to Sheffey, who is an expert on the hauntings in the Martha Washington Inn, the "lady in white" is the ghost known by the name of Beth. Apparently she had been a student at Martha Washington College during the War Between The States and was party to a tragic love affair.

A Yankee spy was captured in Abingdon, Sheffey said, but not without a valiant struggle. In the process of capture, the spy, Captain John Stover, was shot and gravely wounded. He was carried into room No. 60 on the third floor of Preston Hall (now Room 403 on the fourth floor).

Most of the girls had gone home for the Christmas holidays, but some remained to serve as nurses. At the time, the college also served as a makeshift hospital. One of those who stayed behind was Beth.

Beth cared for the wounded man and, in the process, fell in love with him.

For months, Beth tried to nurse her Yankee lover back to health. Beth often sang to comfort him. Sometimes she played her violin.

But instead of getting better, Captain Stover's condition grew worse. Toward the end, he became delirious and unable to speak a coherent sentence. Still, Beth continued to nurse him, never giving up hope that he would recover.

Finally, in his last moment, he clasped Beth's hand and cried, "Beth, don't leave me! I love you!" Then he died.

Now, as Paul Harvey says, here's the rest of the story.

After Stover died, Beth picked up her violin and began to play a mournful little tune. Just as she finished, a Confederate Captain entered the room. The following exchange is supposed to have taken place between them:

"Beth, my dear—I'm sorry, but we've got to take this man."

"Stop," she commanded. "He has been pardoned, Sir, by an officer higher than even Robert E. Lee. Captain Stover is dead."

Then she fainted dramatically into the Confederate's arms.

Melody Bowers has been a housekeeper at the Martha Washington Inn for 26 years, and she has much to say about the ghosts that lurk there. Recently I sat in the Governor's Suite, on the third floor of The Inn, and listened to her and Pete Sheffey swap stories about their experiences.

"One of the jobs of a housekeeper is to knock on the door of each room at the end of the day to see whether the room is vacant," Bowers said. "One day I was just outside the room which used to be number 401 before the 1984 renovation. The wooden floor inside was creaking like someone was walking on it. I knocked on the door, but there was no answer. I knocked again. The same thing. Then I opened the door and looked inside the room. It was empty."

Other times, Bowers said she's heard water running in rooms. Once, she heard water running and couldn't find the source. Then former students of Martha Washington College told her that a room had once existed there, but it had since been sealed off. The room, of course, would have existed when Beth attended the school.

On another occasion Bowers was working on the fourth floor in a room at the end of the hall. Once again, she heard water running. Something unseen had turned on the faucet in a basin, and the room was flooding. Could it have been the ghost of Beth wetting a cold towel to place on her wounded lover's forehead?

Both Sheffey and Bowers agreed that most of the unexplained events at the Martha Washington Inn occur in winter. Although no dates are confirmed, Captain Stover may have been wounded during the rout on the morning of December 15, when Confederate troops attacked the Federals gathered around Clark's blacksmith shop. Then, later, he could have been brought to Beth to be nursed back to health.

Tradition says that Stover lingered on quite a while before he died—possibly three or four months. That would have taken his suffering, and Beth's nursing, through the entire winter. Hence the haunting of the Martha Washington Inn would be more noticeable in the winter.

That explanation, however, accounts for only one ghost at the Martha Washington Inn. "Ghost logic" indicates that a spirit follows a *modus operandi,* or a predictable pattern of behavior. Usually a ghost replicates an event experienced in its lifetime. In Beth's case, it is the apparition of a "lady in white" (symbolic of a nurse?) and the occasional phantom violin music drifting through the building. However, the mysterious footfalls could belong to any one of the other ghosts rumored to haunt the place. Hauntings at the Martha Washington Inn are not new. They have been going on for some time.

Sheffey's grandfather, Wiley Henry, began working in the building in 1900 while it was still a women's college. At the time, the kitchen existed in the area where The Pub is now located—on the first floor. According to local tradition, slaves were once kept in the room. In fact, rumor even has it that bodies of slaves are actually buried in one of the walls.

One day, some of the help were cleaning up the kitchen. All of a sudden one of the men screamed and dropped a pile of pots and pans that he was carrying. Then he ran out the door. Later, he told his co-workers that he had seen the ghost of a former slave, floating toward him.

In 1937, Sheffey's grandfather had a personal experience with another ghost. It was late at night and Henry was walking down the second floor hall, checking the building. In his hand he carried a lantern. Over his shoulder was slung a time clock that he would punch when he reached each station of his security tour.

Suddenly his lantern blew out. Then something appeared. It looked like a ragged, muddy Confederate soldier, horribly wounded and hobbling along on a crutch. A ball had apparently taken off half of his head.

Understandably, Henry didn't linger. He ran for help. When he returned, a pile of fresh mud lay on the carpet—just about where the sales office is now.

Sometimes experiences at the Martha Washington Inn go beyond merely seeing or hearing a ghost. Eva Yarber was the former night auditor at the Inn. Early one morning, her work for the night finished, she walked out into the lobby and sat down in one of the plush chairs beside the roaring fireplace to relax and read the newspaper.

Yarber remembered the day as being George Washington's birthday—and it was cold outside.

Tonight Eva had a young woman, whose name was Glenda, training with her. As both sat by the fire, Glenda became sleepy and dozed off in her chair.

Suddenly, Eva heard someone walking around the lobby. Then she heard a noise at the top of the stairs, and a smoky mist began descending the grand staircase. When the mist reached the bottom, it disappeared around the corner and into another room. The shape was indistinct, but Eva said the figure reminded her of something she had seen before—the creature in the movie **Predator**!

This happened four times—the figure descending the stairs and disappearing into another room. Each time it happened, Eva called out to Glenda, but the sleeping girl didn't stir. She tried stomping. That didn't help either. Then Eva realized she was not making a sound. Nor could she move. *Something was holding her down!*

"Then at about 5:45 in the morning, whatever was holding me let go," Eva said. "I called to Glenda who awoke. I asked her if she had heard me shouting, but she hadn't heard a thing."

"There are a lot of odd things that go on in the Inn, especially when it's cold outside," said Lisa Owens, the buyer for the gift shop. "Strange things that I really can't explain.

"Now the gift shop stays open until 10 at night, and sometimes I work until then. This particular night it was snowing outside and no one had come into the shop since 7:30. I was reading a book, trying to pass the time until it was time to go home. In the gift shop we have a selection of musical rabbits—music boxes. You wind them up and they play a little tune—but you have to wind them up first.

"There's something else you need to know about the gift shop, too. No matter what the temperature outside, that room is always hot. The merchandise is lit with spotlights, and it gets pretty warm.

"About 9:30, it suddenly got very cold in the room—just like a refrigerator. And two of the music boxes on the shelves began playing by themselves. There had been no one in the shop—no one except me—for the past two hours. And these music boxes just started to play all by themselves. Well I got so scared that I went home early that night."

Of course, the ghosts of the Martha Washington Inn have never harmed a soul, nor are they malevolent. The ghosts are a part of a world that fascinates the living—probably because that world is so mysterious and unexplored.

And in this modern, scientific society, when we *think* we know *all* the answers, isn't it exciting to discover that there are still questions?

The Watchful Ghost
of the *Abingdon Virginian*

Editor Martha Weisfeld swears the ghost of a former journalist watches over her and her weekly newspaper. At odd hours, footsteps and other ghostly sounds are heard overhead on the empty second floor. An otherworldly presence is felt. But instead of being frightened, Martha Weisfeld is comforted by the ghostly footfalls and the unseen presence. She believes the ghost is benevolent—a "watch ghost," so to speak.

Before Martha bought the *Abingdon Virginian*, the paper was owned and operated by Woodrum Haynes "Wood" Lyon. Martha believes it's his spirit that haunts the old Greenway Brothers Building, where the newspaper is located.

"Wood was dedicated," Martha said. "He was an old time newspaper man. He typed with two fingers and was dedicated to this office. I'm comforted by him being here."

However, other staff members are not so sure if they want a ghost peeking over their shoulders while they're trying to work. They don't take too kindly to supernatural shenanigans from unseen visitors. Some have become so unnerved, they have threatened to quit on the spot.

Built in 1878 by James C. and David C. Greenway and Thomas Trigg, the Greenway Brothers Building—an ancient wood and brick structure—suffers its share of moans and groans. But if someone were to suggest building stresses as the real source of the strange noises, he would probably get an argument from Martha Weisfeld. She's very protective of her ghost.

Martha bought the *Abingdon Virginian* from the Lyon estate in 1976.

She did it, she said, by spending six months in court dealing with Wood's heirs.

When she first operated the the paper, type was set on an ancient linotype machine, and each edition was printed in the back room. Martha streamlined the operation. She converted to cold type and jobbed out the printing to another firm. Then, for the next 16 years, she earned a reputation as a hard-nosed journalist, not afraid to take on "city hall." And all the time the ghost of Wood Lyon watched over her.

I met Martha Weisfeld on a cool day in October. It was one of those nostalgic days, in a place that reminded a person of small-town America. At any time of the year, Abingdon gives a person that impression. But today was special. Even the trees in town cooperated by adorning their spreading branches with dots of red, gold, and yellow.

Martha was late coming to the office, so I sat in an old wooden rocker waiting for her. I killed time by making a mental note of the layout of her office. The office, like the town, was steeped in nostalgia.

A bookcase covered one entire wall and was stuffed with volumes on every conceivable subject. Directly in front of me were the old desk and cash register used by Wood Lyon. To my right was Martha's own wooden desk, covered with neat stacks of papers; in the center was a mound of unopened mail. A television sat on a nearby shelf, but there was no sign of a computer or word processor.

I developed a mental picture of Martha Weisfeld, based on the appearance of her office. I saw a little old lady, draped in a shapeless dress, wearing granny glasses, face furrowed with age. I couldn't wait to meet this icon from the past.

"She should already be here," her assistant informed me. "We sent someone to get her a half hour ago."

"I knew it!" I thought to myself. Any minute I expected a horse and buggy to draw up to the front door and the afore-described woman helped down by some gallant male dressed in faded overalls.

Five minutes later, Martha Weisfeld swept into the office. She wore a stylish blue outfit, topped off with a matching hat. She looked like she had just stepped from the pages of a J.C. Penney catalog.

"No one comes to work at a country newspaper dressed to the nines," I thought to myself. "At least, no country newspaper I know of!"

Maybe my surprise was ill-concealed, because Martha glared at me impatiently beneath arched eyebrows. She was going to let me know right off who was boss. She controlled our interview from the very beginning. It didn't take me long to realize Martha Weisfeld was no ordinary woman.

"My son is James Monaco, the writer," she told me as she settled easily into a chair across from where I sat. "That's his book down there."

A thick volume titled **Dictionary of Film** topped a stack of other books piled on the floor.

"He wrote that with a couple of other people," Martha continued proudly. "He's writing a book on his own right now. I bought this newspaper in hopes that someday he'll take it over."

Then Martha turned the conversation to the haunting of the *Abingdon Virginian*.

"I'm not afraid of being haunted," Martha said confidently. "I consider it a blessing. Wood Lyon is watching over me and this newspaper. I believe that it's because of his ghost that I have had few financial problems with the publication.

"Everyone around here has heard the footsteps—even my husband, Charles. Wood lived on the second floor when he operated the paper years ago."

"Have you ever gone upstairs to investigate the noises?" I asked.

"No," Martha answered. "And even if I did, I don't think I'd see anything. But Wood's there just the same. I get energy from his spirit. I feel the ghost supports me. He never lets me get discouraged. He comforts me."

She is so earnest about her ghost that a person *has* to believe her—or, at least, *believe* that *she* believes it.

Wood Lyon is not the only ghost who has comforted Martha Weisfeld in times of trouble. There was another a few years back.

"I live on Valley Street in a wonderful old house," she began. "About eight years ago—on a Sunday night—I returned home. I wasn't feeling well and went directly to bed. Upstairs we have dormer windows. It was raining hard that night.

"I was nearly asleep when I saw my mother's face at the window. From what I could see of her torso, she was wearing the same dress we buried her in. And I saw her as plainly as I see you right now.

"She told me not to worry, that everything was going to be all right."

I asked Martha if she was frightened by the apparition.

"It took me months to get over it," she replied with a nervous smile.

Martha's personal philosophy about the supernatural borders on belief in reincarnation.

"We're bonded to people on this earth," she said. "Did you ever meet someone for the first time, but swear you've known them from before? I often get feelings like that.

"Once I met a man and shook hands with him. I suddenly found myself affectionately patting the back of his hand, something I wouldn't have done to a perfect stranger. But I felt that I knew him."

Plainly, Martha Weisfeld's ties with the supernatural are strong. And she certainly has had enough experience with the netherworld in her lifetime, considering her experiences with her mother, as well as the ghost of Wood Lyon.

And some townspeople have no doubt that the ghost of Wood Lyon *really does* watch over her and her weekly newspaper. Certainly the *Abingdon Virginian* has been enormously successful since her takeover 16 years ago. Circulation, for instance, has increased from 2,500 to about 5,500—very respectable growth for a small-town weekly.

You could almost say when Martha Weisfeld bought the *Abingdon Virginian*, the paper *really did* have a ghost of a chance.

"It was a dark and stormy night...."
The Ghosts of Cave House

Just how many ghosts haunt Cave House is unknown. Some say only one. Others claim a whole family of spirits infests the place.

So far no one has seen an apparition at Cave House. But odd noises are heard, especially when the weather is dark and stormy. Strange odors drift through rooms. And in some parts of the house, one gets an eerie feeling—like something is in the room, watching.

Cave House, and the land on which it stands, boasts a colorful history. When Daniel Boone and Nathaniel Gist camped near the property in 1760, their dogs were set upon by ravenous wolves. A large cave was found to serve as a den for the animals. Boone named the area "Wolf Hill."

Cave House, itself, was built by Adam Hickman in 1857. Hickman was a tanner, who also operated a gristmill at the mouth of Wolf Creek. Later the house came into the possession of the White family. In 1949 Cave House was sold to Alice Brock Hilton, widow of novelist James Hilton, the author of **Lost Horizon**.

Like her husband, Alice Hilton was a great supporter of the arts, especially Abingdon's famous Barter Theatre. During the Great Depression, Robert Porterfield gathered a group of out-of-work actors and brought them to Abingdon. There he produced plays in the former town hall and opera house. Underneath the stage was the jail where prisoners were kept for many years, even while the theater was in full operation. On the roof was a fire whistle whose wail brought an unexpected intermission to many a performance. Admission to plays was by barter, in produce or livestock. Barter Theatre was later designated as "The State Theatre of Virginia."

Although James Hilton, himself, never lived in Abingdon, Mrs. Hilton moved there after her husband's death. She allowed Porterfield to use Cave House as living quarters for actors and stagehands.

One of the residents of Cave House in the early days of the Barter Theatre was actor Ernest Borgnine. But he slept there only part of the night. He left, refusing to spend the night again. He gave no explanation for his behavior. Had Borgnine seen or heard the ghosts of Cave House?

When the Holston Mountain Arts and Crafts Cooperative formed in 1971, Cave House was turned into an arts and crafts department store. That's when the haunting began in earnest. Could it be that the ghosts objected to the influx of visitors in their home? Many believed this to be the case. The ghosts always seem to react most when a stranger appears in Cave House.

Sondra Blevins isn't the kind of woman who scares easily, nor is she intimidated or concerned that Cave House might be haunted. But she heard stories from others—similarly sound of mind—about mysterious doings in Cave House. It was only a matter of time until something extraordinary happened to her.

"Things happen most often when it is dark and raining outside," she said. She told me about a former weekend shop manager, Charles McThenia, who worked in the craft shop 13 years.

He told Sondra he had heard ghosts in the house many times—footsteps, stomping, and the unmistakable sound of tables and chairs being dragged across the floor of the upper stories. He had smelled phantom odors of bread baking, meat frying, even sulphur.

One day he walked into the shop and found everything rearranged. Then, on one dark and rainy Sunday afternoon, Charles McThenia had a particularly frightening experience.

Few customers had visited the shop that day, and for most of the afternoon McThenia was alone. The noises began with a loud stomping overhead. McThenia checked the second and third floor but found nothing—only empty rooms and shadows.

Upon returning to the first floor, he heard the distinctive, unmistakable sound of a broomstick falling over and hitting the floor—again and again. Once more, McThenia searched for a possible explanation. There was no one else in Cave House.

The noises continued all afternoon and McThenia grew more nervous. Finally he could take it no longer. He walked to his car and got his gun. When he returned a few minutes later the noises still continued overhead, but McThenia felt secure. After all, he was armed and....

Then McThenia looked at the gun in his hand and realized how vulnerable he really was. "This is ridiculous," he thought to himself. "How can I shoot what I can't see?"

McThenia left Cave House that night, thoroughly shaken and vowing never to return. But later that evening, in the safety of his home, McThenia reconsidered his decision. He had worked in Cave House 10 years and the ghosts had not harmed him yet, although they had had plenty of opportunity. So he returned to Cave House and worked in the craft shop three more years.

Now Sondra Blevins is more philosophical about the ghosts of Cave House. Since the cave zigzags beneath the building, she thinks this might account for some of the noises she's heard.

"Furthermore," she told me, "the building is old. Squirrels and pigeons often get into the upper stories. That might account for some of the noises."

Blevins also had an explanation for the odors that sometimes permeate the house. "I think the smells of bread and meat cooking might come from neighboring houses," she said. "Actually, Charles McThenia is the only one that I know who's smelled the sulphur."

When Sondra Blevins hears strange, unexplained noises in the house, she usually ignores them. But one time the sounds really set her teeth on edge.

"It was in the summer, five or six years ago, during the Highlands Festival, and on one of the first nights we stayed open late," she began. "Usually we were only open during the day.

"Charles and his wife, Corey, stopped by, thinking that a woman alone might need some reassurance. That night, Charles told me his account of that ghostly afternoon when he was tending the store alone.

"Later on, after Charles and his wife had left, I distinctly heard footsteps walking across the front porch. I looked outside, but no one was there. Then I heard the sound of tables and chairs scraping across the second floor.

"Also I heard the sound of a pebble or bead dropping and rolling across the floor on an upper story. I noticed that each time a customer would arrive, the noises would stop. Then, when they left, the noises would start again."

Tina Jennings is a criminal justice major at Virginia Highlands Community College. She considers herself sensitive to the presence of ghosts. She began work in Cave House Craft Shop the first week of May 1992.

"I didn't know anything about the stories or about the haunting at first," she said. "I hadn't heard anything at all."

On her first day in the craft shop, she was working at the top of the back stairs when she suddenly had the feeling of being watched. "It was like someone was curious as to who I was. Then I felt very cold."

There really is a "cold spot" in Cave House. I've felt it, myself. It's located in the rear of the building near the stairs. There's not a great drop in temperature. In fact, many customers walk through it every day without noticing. But Tina and I—and some others—feel the difference.

Since I'm a folklorist and not a ghost hunter (although I'm often accused of being the latter), I endeavor to keep an open mind when recording stories that others tell, trying not to make judgments as to whether they are true or not. This goes especially for ghostlore. In fact, I'm not even sure whether I believe in ghosts. But I cannot deny I had *my own* unnerving encounter in Cave House.

During my research for this chapter, I had heard much about the mysterious noises and other ghostly happenings on the second and third floor. When Tina told me about her feeling of being watched, I just had to visit the second floor and see for myself.

Tina accompanied me up the staircase. At the top, a door to the right led to a storeroom. Tina opened the door and suggested I go inside. As soon as I stepped over the threshold, I had a strong feeling which I can describe best as a combination of fear and dread. *I knew something was in that room with me*—almost as if I had surprised it by walking in—and it was not merely curious as to who I was. It, whatever *it* was, resented my intrusion!

I turned and ran down the stairs, Tina close at my heels. As I said, my attitude is generic when it comes to the possibility of the existence of ghosts. But I was also very certain—there was no doubt of it in my mind—that you couldn't pay me enough to spend a night in Cave House.

Others say they have had similar experiences—the feeling of being watched by unseen eyes, especially near the back stairs and on the second and third floor. But *whose* eyes? Who, or what, haunts Cave House? And how many?

There is a very odd photograph hanging on the wall near the cash register on the first floor of Cave House. Sondra Blevins says the photo is of the White family, who occupied Cave House about the turn of the century.

Adam Hickman's daughter, Ann Eliza, had married Francis Campbell. Her father had died in 1862 after suffering 10 years of ill heath. Then, on her death, Ann Hickman Campbell willed the property to Kathleen R. White. The house remained in the White family until 1949, the year Alice Hilton bought it.

The old photograph contains the images of Madge, Annie, Kathleen, Posey, Gay, and Grandmother White. Cradled in Granny's arms is Baby Windham White. So what, you say? So what is so odd about a family photograph?

Well, most striking are the expressions of the people in the photo. In pictures of that era, more often than not, subjects held a solemn expression. The reason for this was the low sensitivity of the orthochromatic film of the time. Long exposures were necessary to obtain a clear image, and the subject had to hold very still for several seconds, or the picture would blur. Solemn expressions are much easier to hold than smiles.

Although smiles in turn-of-the-century photos are not unknown, the expressions on these women's faces go far beyond that. Several of them actually seem to be caught in the act of laughing. This is not only highly unusual in such a portrait, *it's unheard of!*

As far as I can discover, the Whites were a large and happy family who loved their home. Tina Jennings believes it is the ghosts of some—or even all—of these women who haunt Cave House. "They are just curious about who comes in here," Jennings said. "That's why people have strange feelings about being watched. After all, *this is their home!*"

If this is true, Cave House is not filled with malevolent spirits. Rather, the structure is inhabited by a coterie of women who, just like you or I, would be more than curious if a stranger walked into our home.

In the case of the "buttinsky" folklorist who sticks his nose in where it's not wanted, the attitude of the ghosts of Cave House goes beyond mere curiosity. Those ghosts wanted me out of their home—*all the way out!*

At the time, I was more than happy to oblige!

The Ghosts of the Barter Theatre

Some folks think no less than two ghosts haunt the famous Barter Theatre in Abingdon. One of them is identified as the shade of the theater's founder, the amiable Robert Porterfield. The other is a malevolent, unnamed spirit that has chased no less a person than actor Ned Beatty from his dressing room—and chased him clear out into the street.

Theaters traditionally act as a magnet for ghosts. All the very best theaters have at least one. Theaters in England, for example, are famous for their haunts—like the famous "Gray Man" of Drury Lane.

The fact that Barter Theatre's founder haunts the theater building on Main Street should come as no surprise to anyone; Porterfield put his heart and soul into the theater when he was alive. Nor should it be any real surprise that a second, more horrifying spirit haunts the old building—considering its checkered history.

The building that presently houses Abingdon's Barter Theatre was built in the 1830s as the Sinking Springs Presbyterian Church. Later it was operated by the Sons of Temperance and became known far and wide as Temperance Hall.

The building also served as a theater. The great actor Edwin Booth was said to have once trod its boards. And at the same time Booth performed upstairs, a male institute met in the basement.

By 1905 the building was in a terrible state of decay. The structure had been passed on to the Town of Abingdon by trustees of the Sons of Temperance. They no longer needed it. Bonds were issued to repair and enlarge the building. With bond money, a new front was attached. Then the building was employed as Abingdon City Hall, and it was still used as such when Robert Porterfield brought his Barter Theatre to town in the spring of 1933.

Robert Porterfield was born in 1905 near Austinville in Wythe County. Although his father wanted Robert to be a preacher, the boy was lured by the call of the stage. Forsaking his father's wishes, young Porterfield attended the Academy of Dramatic Arts in New York. Later he paid his dues as an actor by accepting small bits and walk-on roles in dozens of Broadway shows in the late '20s and early '30s.

The Great Depression hit Broadway late with a vengeance. Hundreds of actors were thrown out of work. Shows closed the same week they opened. Production money was scarce, and few successful shows were produced.

Once-busy actors were forced to accept charity. An "Actor's Dinner Club" was set up in the basement of Union Methodist Church in New York. Every night, out-of-work thespians would gather, eat, swap stories, and talk shop. This was early in 1933.

Being from Southwest Virginia, Porterfield knew that food was plentiful on the farms that dotted the countryside. So in the spring of that year, the young actor brought 22 out-of-work New York actors to Abingdon. There they would establish a theater and barter produce for plays.

The success of Porterfield and his Barter Theatre is well-known. Barter alumni who have gone on to bigger and better things include Gregory Peck, Patricia Neal, Ernest Borgnine, Frank Lovejoy, Ned Beatty, Claude Akins, and Hume Cronyn. Barter Theatre is still very much in operation under its second director, Rex Partington. Porterfield died of a heart attack in 1971.

Almost immediately after his death, sightings of the ghost of Bob Porterfield began.

Porterfield has been seen almost everywhere in the theater building. He has been observed in almost every kind of dress, but most often in the gray sweater he was so fond of. Because of this, his shade has been dubbed "The Gray Ghost."

Actors performing on stage have also seen him sitting in the audience, wearing a white dinner jacket—attire that he always wore on opening nights.

In his book **The Barter Theatre Story**, Mark Dawidziak quotes a personal encounter from actress Cleo Holladay.

"I had a long, long scene (in **Silent Night, Lonely Night**) where I had to lie in bed on stage. The audience couldn't really see my face, but I could look up from my angle and see the kids in the light booth. One night I looked up at them and in the last row was a man in a white dinner jacket.... I'm convinced it was Bob. I know it was. That was the same night the pipes rattled and we took it as a sign that Bob approved of the show."

Another time, one of the stagehands was walking by the theater and saw a man in a gray sweater sitting on a stoop outside the building. "Hi, Bob," the man said. Then he realized Bob Porterfield had been dead for several years. When he looked back, the figure was gone.

Sometimes guests in the Martha Washington Inn, across the street from the theater, look out their room window late at night to see the figure of a man inside the theater. The vision is always accompanied by a light—sometimes white, sometimes red—behind the figure. Mark Dawidziak tells the story of Barter apprentice David Lohoefer, who had just such a chilling experience.

According to Dawidziak, Lohoefer called veteran character actor and director Owen Phillips, a good friend of Porterfield's, when he saw a figure inside the theater early one morning.

"Owen, you'd better get down here.... There's somebody fooling around inside the theater."

"Just relax," Phillips told him. "Calm down. It was probably just Mr. P. I wouldn't advise going into the theater. Just go home."

This incident, too, occurred during the run of **Silent Night, Lonely Night**, three years, to the month, after Porterfield's death.

As for the malevolent ghost in the Barter Theatre—no one has seen it. But it can be felt. Like Ned Beatty's encounter, its presence fills the living with dread and deadly danger. And no one knows its identity—but it certainly *is not Bob Porterfield.*

The best guess is the ghost—perhaps "presence" is a better word—is that of a vindictive entity that strikes terror in the heart of everyone who encounters it. Barter publicity director Lou Flanigan told Mark Dawidziak of his near miss with the specter one terrifying night a few years ago.

"I was working stage right and the only exit was stage left. All of a sudden, I felt a presence. I felt that I had to get out of there. I just had this horrible feeling that something was really going to get me. I ran across the stage, threw open the door, ran around the scene dock, down the stairs, into the dressing room area, and to the stage door that leads to the alley. If I had turned around and seen it, it probably would have been fatal. It was like it was following me. Then I couldn't get the door open. I started kicking it, and finally it opened and I ran up the alley to Main Street. One second more and I'm sure it would have grabbed me. When I looked back, I saw that the stage door was wide open. I knew I had to go back and close it, but it was a full 15 minutes before I could work up my nerve to do it."

After that night, Lou Flanigan refused ever to be in the theater alone again!

The Mysterious Cat

When my book **Demon In The Woods** came out last year, I was amazed by the number of people who came to me claiming to have seen a Wampas Cat. They were from Tennessee, North Carolina, and Virginia—all over.

One reader told me he had heard his daddy and granddaddy tell stories about the Wampas Cat when he was a boy, but he hadn't heard the subject brought up for years—that is, until I wrote about it.

"I was raised in Wise County," my informant said. "When I was a kid, I heard all kinds of tales about this cat that stood up and walked around on two legs. My daddy even said he saw it once.

"He was out chopping wood one day and he spied the thing, staring at him from a clearing. The cat was about four or five feet tall and stood on two legs. Its eyes were like fire.

"They stood there, watching each other for a couple seconds. Then the cat ambled back into the woods. Daddy told some of his friends about seeing the cat, but they laughed at him. They didn't believe it. He was so embarrassed at being laughed at that he never mentioned the Wampas Cat to anyone again."

"Have you ever seen a Wampas Cat?" I asked.

"Nope. Never did."

"Do you believe that your father saw one?"

"Yes, I do," my reader replied. "Do you?"

Indeed. Can I (or anyone for that matter) believe in such a creature as a Wampas Cat? I *do* believe in the old adage that where there's smoke there's bound to be some fire to go along with it. These people are seeing something—they're not all making it up.

The legend of the Wampas Cat is one of the most persistent stories in Southwest Virginia and East Tennessee. The cat that walks on two legs has been seen from Chattanooga to Roanoke. The Wampas Cat is an enigmatic, magical creature—appearing and, then, disappearing in an instant.

The creature appears peaceful. So far, I haven't heard of anyone who has been attacked. The cat is merely curious about Homo sapiens.

Tales of the Wampas Cat are so far spread, and people believe in them so earnestly, that it is certainly hard not to accept the possibility that such a creature exists.

No more than one Wampas Cat has ever been seen at a time. In fact, I believe there is only one Wampas Cat—and that it is a ghost.

Here's why.

There's an old Cherokee Indian legend about a young woman who ventured out into the woods to face a demon. Covering her face was a mask given to her by an Adawehis, or Cherokee conjurer. The mask was actually the preserved face of a wildcat and, with this, she was supposed to frighten the demon. According to the legend, the woman defeated the demon—scared him so bad that he fled through the woods to escape the strange apparition before him. The sight of the woman, wearing the wildcat's face, must have looked very similar to the traditional appearance of a Wampas Cat.

Could the Wampas Cat be, in reality, the spirit of this Indian woman, roaming through the woods, looking for more demons to chase?

As I said before, a lot of people have claimed to have seen a Wampas Cat. In Southwest Virginia, I have been told of sightings in most of the towns and cities, as well as in the countryside. Even Abingdon, itself, has been visited by the cat who walks on its hind legs.

Several years ago, Tim Smith of Bristol was a guest at the Martha Washington Inn. Abingdon is a wonderful place for quiet, late-night walks. Tim and his wife decided to stroll down Main Street about eleven o'clock one night.

"We were heading east and just walked off the lawn at the Martha Washington. I glanced across the street toward the Barter Theatre. There's this little road right next to it (Goodman Alley) and there's a metal fire escape on the side of the building, toward the front.

"Well, I looked over there and thought I saw two eyes peering at me through the iron steps. They didn't look like human eyes—more like that of a cat.

"I had heard a lot about the ghosts that are supposed to haunt the Barter Theatre, so I said to my wife, 'Look, Jean, there's one of those Barter ghosts that I was telling you about.'

"Well, she laughed. And I threw up my hand and yelled across the street, 'Hello there, Mr. Ghost!'

"I heard a hiss like a cat does when it's warning an enemy to stay away. The eyes disappeared, and I saw the back end of something running down beside the building and disappear into the darkness. I asked my wife if she had seen it, too. When she said she had, I asked her what it looked like to her.

" 'You're going to think I'm crazy,' she said.

" 'Try me.'

" 'Well, from where I was standing it looked like a huge cat running away from us, on its hind legs.' "

The Mystery of Ghostly Vera

Students call her "Vera." The very mention of her name strikes fear in the hearts of those who dare trod the corridors of Main Hall of Virginia Intermont College after dark. The identity of the ghost is said to be a young girl who died a tragic death while attending college there in the 1920s.

For 70 years, legends persisted that her ghost wandered the nebulous halls of VI after dark. Vera was both seen and heard. She was VI's most famous—and most infamous—ghost.

One of the first things incoming VI freshmen heard was the tragic story of Vera—her scandalous love affair, her suicide, and the fire that resulted when her body, which dangled at the end of a noose, knocked over lighted candles.

Nearly everyone who knew the story also felt sure they knew the ghost's identity. Legends and stories about her were spun by generation after generation of wide-eyed students. Numerous accounts of the ghost appeared in print—including VI's own official alumni newspaper.

The story of Vera was so down pat that it seemed like nothing could shake it until...

...the real Vera turned up. VI officials spoke with her on the phone. Unless AT&T has strung lines into the netherworld, at this writing Vera is alive and well and living in Texas!

Virginia Intermont spokesman Jeff Prince told me Vera remembers little about her stay at VI. She attended only a year. He doesn't know for sure, but he thinks she completed her education elsewhere, possibly at a

Christian college somewhere in Missouri.

Furthermore, she is unaware that she has become a legend on campus and was thought dead for 70 years, a victim of her own hand. That's not the kind of news you suddenly spring on a 92-year-old woman.

The administration at Virginia Intermont College was philosophical about the legend before the truth about "Vera" was known, treating the story rather lightheartedly. They see no reason to change their policy, even after recent revelations about Vera's longevity.

"We still like the legend of Vera here at the college," Jeff Prince told me. "And we plan to keep it going."

So much for squashing a good legend.

I can hear the anguished groans of readers now. Have we been conned by a folktale gotten out of hand? I don't think so. Only the name has been changed, although Jeff said the college is still willing to refer to the ghost as "Vera."

By all reports, something otherworldly still roams Virginia Intermont College. There are enough eyewitness reports to verify that fact. But who is this creature of the night? The only thing we can be absolutely sure of—at least as far as identity is concerned—is who the ghost is not.

The haunting seems to center around a mysterious room on the third floor of Main Hall. According to legend, there was once a fire in the room. Furthermore, each time renovations have been attempted on the room, another fire has broken out.

(I have visited the room and could find no evidence of fire. The room is presently used as storage. VI officials say the room is located in a part of Main Hall that is very difficult to heat.)

Strange events have also been reported to take place in the room.

Virginia Intermont College has been in existence for over 100 years. In 1884, the Rev. J.R. Harrison erected a $10,000 wooden building at Glade Springs—a new Christian college for young women. Funds to build came from as far away as Kentucky, West Virginia, and Tennessee—from all kinds of people.

At first called Southwest Virginia Institute, the school opened in the fall of that year. Thirteen boarding students occupied the dormitory wing. The rest of the student body commuted from nearby towns and farms. There were three full-time faculty that first year.

The new school grew faster than anyone had anticipated, and the governing board decided to move the campus to nearby Bristol, a more central location. Land overlooking the town was purchased for $7,500. A large main building, nicknamed "Wood's Castle" (named for Thomas Wood, who had provided the school heavy financial support), was raised, and the new school opened for business in the fall of 1893 as Virginia Institute.

After the turn of the century, the name of the school was changed, once again, to Virginia Intermont College.

Main Hall is a Victorian-style building that has changed little over the years. In fact, it's the very image of the traditional haunted house. Students still reside in Main Hall, although not close to the infamous haunted room on the third floor. During the summer, when the dormitory is empty, is the most frightening time to be in the building, according to former VI security guard Jamie Smith.

"None of the security guards like to work the graveyard shift in Main Hall," Smith said. "I wouldn't work the graveyard shift over there again. You couldn't pay me enough."

Admittedly, the haunted room is in one of the spookiest parts of the building. The room sits alone, at the end of a hall. Just past the room is a breezeway that connects Main Hall to East Hall. It's dark up there, even in broad daylight.

Smith reported that hall and room lights flash on and off without apparent reason. Things in the haunted room move around by themselves. Objects suddenly turn up missing.

"One time I walked by the room and there was a bare table sitting in the middle of the floor," Smith said. "A minute later, I returned to find the same table set for dinner."

Sometimes the apparition of a young woman stands at the dormer window, looking out on campus. Behind her, ghostly red flames are seen, which leap up from the floor and lick the ceiling.

"I really got nervous staying in the building at night," Smith added. And every time her rounds took her past the haunted room, Smith said she would lower her head and stare at the floor as she walked by. She was afraid of what she might see if she glanced in there.

That's when Smith said she took to hanging crosses around her neck to help ward off possible assaults from the supernatural.

The day after I talked to Jamie Smith about her chilling experiences with the room, I met a VI graduate who admitted she'd missed a whole semester because of the ghost. She asked not to be identified, so I'll call her "Jane."

This is her story.

"I had heard stories about the ghost in Main Hall," Jane began, "but I was adventurous when I was 18. The prospect of living in a haunted dormitory excited me, and I hoped that one day I'd actually get to see the ghost."

Then she frowned. "If I knew then what I know now, I wouldn't have been so anxious.

"My room was on the second floor of Main Hall. I was supposed to have had a roommate, but she never showed up at the beginning of school—something about finances. So I had the place all to myself.

"Two months passed; nothing. I was beginning to think the whole story was a lot of hooey. The other girls kept talking about missing things and blaming the thefts on someone named Vera. I heard that was the name they had given the ghost—but nothing of mine ever disappeared.

"Along about Halloween, we spent the evening telling ghost stories down in the lounge. Some of the tales of our ghost—the one they called Vera—were included. We all sat around in a circle with lighted candles, in the dark, and all that. It was very spooky.

"Most of us went to bed at midnight and, of course, I was alone in my room.

"One of the things I remembered hearing about the ghost was that its activities were not necessarily confined to the haunted room or the hallway outside. The general consensus of opinion was that it roamed all over campus.

"Well, I got undressed and slipped into my pajamas. I was kicking myself all the time because I knew that I had a math test the next day and I was getting to bed so late.

"I crawled into bed and snuggled down underneath the covers. Then the room got real cold.

"I opened my eyes and, in the dark, could barely see the door. A mist appeared, like a luminous electrically charged cloud. Slowly it formed into the shape of a young girl—just her head and torso, no legs. Then the ghost floated in my direction.

"I started to scream but was horrified to discover my body was paralyzed. I couldn't have moved or made a sound, even if I had wanted to—which I very much did!

"The apparition stopped about three or four feet from my bed and just hung there in midair. Those eyes were staring...just staring at me...unblinking...it was horrible. All I could do at the time was stare back, compelled to watch.

"After what seemed like an eternity, the vision slowly dispersed back into the cloud until it vanished and I was alone again in the room. As soon as I was able, I screamed as long and loud as I could.

"I never stayed in Main Hall after that night. In fact, I dropped out of school and didn't return until the next fall."

Then Jane smiled weakly.

"I'm a successful career woman now and consider myself pretty strong and determined. I've competed in a man's world for years. It's been rough, but I held up. I'm really proud of what I've accomplished, and I credit VI for starting me on the right road. But I almost didn't return to school after that night—after my experience with the ghost.

"But after the few months it took me to get over the experience, I realized that the supernatural is just another part of the world we live in. It might be frightening to experience it, but you have to accept it because it's so real.

"In my case, I accepted it so well that I never set foot in Main Hall again—unless I had absolutely no choice in the matter."

Now the question remains—who is the ghost of the young girl seen on the campus of Virginia Intermont College. Since the most likely candidate for the haunting has been eliminated once and for all, and the legend surrounding the tragic events that brought her to her alleged "end" have been scotched forever, where do we turn now for answers?

Folklore is like a bureaucracy—it's self-perpetuating. I suspect that tales of Vera's ghost will continue at the school. At least, the administration says it will do nothing to discourage the stories. Maybe one day, the true identity of the ghost will surface.

And maybe not.

In the meantime, we can only hope that another startling revelation about the infamous Virginia Intermont ghost stays hidden for just a little while longer.

Murder House

The old house on Johnson Street in Bristol has stood empty for many years. It was first built over a century ago when the city was young—built even before that fateful day in 1895 when the city fathers passed an ordinance banning cowbells within the city limits. It seems the hollow clanking of the bells in the wee hours of the morning disturbed the sleep of some residents.

But cowbells are the least of the noises heard from the old house. And the noises do disturb residents in the early morning hours. Unfortunately, the city government would have a difficult time in banning these particular sounds—that is, unless they had control over the supernatural.

At certain times the terrified screams of a woman are heard echoing through the neighborhood. On other occasions a loud, metallic sound is heard within the building.

Lights appear in the upper story window. Then they move through the structure.

The house has been unoccupied for some time. Not even its owner will live there. Attempts have been made to rent it out, but there are no takers.

Local legend says that a woman was once murdered in the house. Her husband attacked her with a butcher knife. At the time, he was drunk.

After being chased through the rooms in the early hours of the morning, she burst out on the front porch. There, the murderous husband caught up with her, stabbing her repeatedly while she screamed for help. None came.

Then the husband threw the bloody knife on the front lawn and fled into the night. By the time neighbors arrived, the woman was dead. The police later counted 27 stab wounds in her neck, chest, and back.

An all-out search for the husband yielded nothing. He had fled from Bristol and was never seen again. Later, it was reported that he had been killed in a knife fight in Knoxville, but that was never confirmed.

Since the house was a rental property, another tenant moved in shortly after the murder. It was then that the screaming and the lights began in earnest.

Early in the morning, shrieks sliced through the halcyon air. The new tenant, unable to sleep or to keep his frazzled nerves in check, soon moved out. He was only the first of a steady procession of renters who fled in terror from the murder house. Some occupied the house for only hours.

Before long, neighbors began to shun the house too. Ghost lights were seen in the rooms. A mysterious metallic clanking sound echoed through the house. One witness saw a light race through the structure and emerge onto the front porch, where it disappeared. The light reappeared in an upstairs window, raced through the house again, and burst onto the porch again. It disappeared a second time.

One night a group of teenagers decided to visit the house and stay all night. Gaining entry through a rear window, they settled down for the evening. But their visit didn't last long. A half hour later, they rushed out onto the porch and scattered into the night.

Since then, no one has visited the house after dark.

The Campground Road Horror

When Elaine Lang rented the one-story house on Campground Road, located about a mile and a half from Bristol, she might have thought twice about it if she had known in advance what she had gotten herself into. She soon discovered she had leased her worst nightmare.

Campground Road winds through rolling Virginia countryside, rich in dairy farms. Elaine's house sat on top of a little hill, overlooking the bow of a curve. Neighbors around her were sparse. There were no houses across Campground Road—just woods and a creek.

The house was probably built in the '40s or '50s. A long porch extended across the front of the building, which was sheathed in white wood siding. A private driveway stretched up the hill from the road to the house. And sitting right next to the driveway was another house—this one larger, but long-ago abandoned.

"When I rented the house," Elaine said, "my landlady told me that no one could stay there but me and my children. I was a single mother at the time. I had a daughter who was 12 and a son who was 16.

"But the night I moved in I had a girlfriend, Barbara, help me move. Since it had gotten so late, she was planning to spend the night."

Around midnight, when everything had been unloaded, Elaine and Barbara sat in the kitchen eating a late supper. The porch light was on. Suddenly Barbara saw a figure walking up the driveway.

"Oh, Lord," she said. "Here comes your landlady! If she sees me, you're going to be in trouble."

Barbara jumped up and ran back into the house to hide. Elaine went to the door, but no one was there. She looked around outside. No one.

Elaine rejoined her friend and said, "There was nobody out there. You're seeing things."

"I saw her," Barbara protested. "It was a little, gray haired lady. She was walking up your driveway. I thought she was your landlady."

"That doesn't sound like my landlady," Elaine answered. "My landlady's a blonde, and she's far from old."

After that first night, things began to disappear from the house. "You'd come in and set your pocketbook down," Elaine said, "then you'd go back to get it and it wouldn't be there. We never connected anything as supernatural—at least at first. I chalked it up to forgetfulness. I even blamed my kids."

However, it soon became apparent that something was terribly wrong in the house.

In April, Elaine had a friend from North Carolina spend the weekend with her. Elaine had gone to work, and the friend was in the house alone all day. When Elaine returned home from work, the friend had a strange tale to tell.

"I had three small kittens," Elaine explained. "And my friend said that she suddenly discovered the kittens were dripping wet. She added that she went all over the house and couldn't find anywhere where they could have gotten into water. She thought that maybe they had fallen into the toilet. She went to the bathroom first, but the lid was down. The bathtub was dry. The sink was dry. We never did find out how those three kittens got wet."

That wasn't the last time that something strange happened to a cat in the house. And this later contributed to a bizarre theory about how those three kittens had gotten so wet. But more about that later.

The first of June when school let out, Elaine's son went to North Carolina to spend the summer. Only Elaine and her daughter were left in the house.

"The first week he was gone," Elaine remembered, "I was getting ready to take a shower. My daughter was in bed reading. It was so hot that night that we both decided to sleep in my son's room because of the good cross ventilation.

"By that time, I had gotten rid of two of the cats and only had one left. I heard something fall in the living room and I hollered at my daughter. I asked her to find out what the cat had knocked over.

"She yelled back that the cat didn't knock anything over—it was lying beside her on the bed."

Elaine wrapped a towel around herself and peeked into the living room. Sitting on the couch was a little, gray haired lady. She looked solid—not like a ghost.

"If she had stood up," Elaine said, "she wouldn't have been more than five feet tall. She looked like she was wearing an old house dress. She had a kinky, curly permanent. She was sitting hunched with her arms on her knees—bent over."

Although Elaine saw the woman only from the side, she stared straight at her. (Many sightings of apparitions are out of the corner of the eye.) The woman did not turn around and return the stare.

"I didn't believe what I saw," Elaine said. "Seeing is not believing and I didn't believe it. I shook my head, closed my eyes, and looked again. She was still sitting there. Then I said to myself, 'There is no way there's a gray haired lady sitting on my couch.'

"I ignored her and went on into the bathroom and continued my shower."

After completing her shower, Elaine opened the bathroom door to let the steam out. Her cat—the one which had been on her daughter's bed—sauntered through the door. Elaine looked down to speak to it.

Suddenly, the cat was lifted up by unseen hands and hurled backward through the hall, into the living room—a full 30 feet. It landed splayed on the hardwood floor and then skidded up against the wall. The terrified animal leaped up and fled for the nearest haven of safety—underneath the bed.

Elaine couldn't believe her eyes, but she calmly walked into the bedroom and crawled into bed. She said nothing to her daughter about the incident. That would have frightened her.

Elaine then opened a book and began trying to concentrate on reading.

"We were both lying in bed," Elaine remembered, "when all of a sudden my son's closet door flew open with such force that it bounced off the back wall. I got up, walked across the room, and shut the door. I got back in bed, and almost immediately, the door flew open again."

Elaine's daughter was thoroughly shaken. Elaine tried to calm the child by explaining that the wind was banging the door. Elaine got up a second time and shut the door—tight. She pulled on it to make sure it was firmly latched—it wouldn't open. As soon as she crawled into the bed, the door slammed open again.

"My daughter was extremely nervous by this time, because this kind of weirdness affects her. This time, when I got up to shut the door, I looked in the closet, through the clothes, to see if anybody was hiding back there. Nothing in there. I shut it again, hard. Then I sat on the side of the bed, ready to grab anybody who opened the door.

"The minute the door started to open for the fourth time, I ran over and, again, there was nothing in there. Then I picked up the phone and called my mother and asked her whether we could spend the night with her."

Elaine's daughter swore she would never spend another night in the house. She moved in with her grandmother until her mother found another place to live. Elaine, too, resolved never to spend another night in horror house. She made immediate plans to move.

But the terror, for her, was not over yet.

Elaine's brother accompanied her to the house the next day to start packing. He was in one bedroom with some boxes, and Elaine was in the other. A small portable stereo was playing in the hallway. It was a Hank Williams song, "I'm So Lonesome I Could Cry." The volume kept getting louder and louder.

"I thought my brother must have gone deaf," Elaine said. "Just about the same time I came out to ask him to turn the radio down, he came out. I asked him if he was hard of hearing. And he said, 'I'm not the one who turned it up. I thought you did.' "

So Elaine turned the volume down, and they both returned to the bedroom. And the same thing happened again! Elaine turned the radio off and put some records on. And since nothing happened to the record player, and since it was getting late, they decided they would spend the night in the house.

"My brother, at the time, was about 18 years old. We didn't want to sleep together, and we didn't want to sleep separately, so we hauled a mattress into the living room. I slept on the couch facing the kitchen, and he slept on the mattress facing the bedrooms. And we left the light on—just in case.

"Neither one of us was sleeping. We were lying there listening for every little noise. All of a sudden I felt ice cold air over my head.

"The minute I felt the air, he jumped up and said there was a black shadow over my head!

" 'Let's get out of here,' I yelled. 'I have to go to work in the morning, and we're not going to sleep any more in this place!' "

As they began to leave, Elaine thought that she would grab some of the food she had stashed in the freezer and take it over to her mother's house so that it wouldn't spoil. Then she walked out of the house.

"When I reached back in to shut the door, something grabbed my hand. I jerked away, and we ran to get into the car. When I opened the car door and the light came on, I looked down and my hand was bleeding. I mean it was pouring the blood. I tried to get it stopped, but it wouldn't stop bleeding."

Elaine decided she would reenter the house to find something to put on the wound. Both Elaine and her brother returned to the house and ran cold water on the wound, but it still wouldn't stop bleeding. Finally, the pair returned to the car.

The car started down the driveway. When it finally descended the hill and turned onto Campground Road, Elaine looked back to the house.

"I saw the curtains pulled back from one of the windows like someone was standing there, looking out. I saw no one. Just the curtains pulled back. It was then that my hand suddenly stopped bleeding!"

To this day, her hand still bears the scar from that terrifying night!

In the meantime, Elaine had told some other people about the ghostly goings-on in her house. Of course, they didn't believe her. But three of them were kind enough to help Elaine and her brother pack.

Once again, the stereo was on. The music made the job go easier.

"We were playing a stack of records, but something had happened. The records were stuck—the records on the bottom of the stack were not turning. But the music was coming from the speakers. And the radio was definitely not on! All five of us saw it. I called my mother's house, and my sister, Pat, answered the phone. 'You're not going to believe what five of us are sitting here watching,' I said to her."

After that, the house acquired an infamous reputation in Elaine's family and circle of friends. Her sister, Pat, would not set foot in the building, under any circumstances. Even the cat, who was forced to stay in the house because Elaine's mother would not allow a feline to set foot in her own house, became a nervous wreck. Elaine said the animal lost a terrible amount of weight during the month it took them to move.

"I left it plenty of cat food," she said, "but something was terribly wrong. All the cat food was gone when I went to refill her dish. I don't know whether she was eating it or something was taking it from her. But she was definitely starving.

"Things got so bad that I was forced to finally let the cat out. It disappeared and I never saw it again."

Who was the ghost of the little, gray haired lady that haunted horror house? Elaine has no idea, except that it could have been someone connected with the abandoned house next door.

"The house looked like it hadn't been lived in for a long time. Structurally, it wasn't in bad shape; it just looked abandoned. I think that someone might have built this new house—the one I tried to live in— then abandoned the old one."

Though she was thoroughly frightened at the time, today Elaine is philosophical about the ghost in her former house.

"I grew up with stuff like this," she said. "My grandmother lived in a haunted house. She had a harmless ghost there she called Flip-Flop, because of the noises it made walking around the second story while we were on the first.

"I've always looked at it this way. I don't know of anybody who has died that would come back and hurt me. So I'm not afraid of ghosts.

"But I don't like being around them either!"

And what of the three wet kittens that Elaine's friend from North Carolina had discovered in the house one day?

Much of the ghost's wrath had been directed toward cats. First, the cat was thrown backwards from the bathroom into the living room. Then, while trying to move, the same cat was obviously tortured—and perhaps even starved—by someone in the house other than Elaine.

Could it be, therefore, that the ghost of the gray haired old woman hated cats? And, if that is so, is it not plausible that the three kittens were dripping wet from a determined effort to *drown them*?

The Battle For Salt
and
Buried Treasure

Guarding buried treasure seems to occupy the time of some ghosts, with wealth as the great motivator, both in life and in death. Apparently some denizens of the netherworld believe if you can't take it with you then, by heaven, at least you can prevent anyone else from taking it either. A case in point is the Smith treasure, rumored to be buried in a saltpeter cave near Saltville and guarded by a ghost who constantly outsmarts the living.

The treasure ended up in this particular cave as the result of a crisscross double cross involving a Saltville businessman and plantation owner, his son, and a greedy Yankee sergeant.

The story begins in October 1864. General Burbridge was beginning his fourth foray into Southwest Virginia. With 5,000 troops he entered Virginia via Pikeville, Kentucky. His orders were to destroy the mines around Saltville, thereby cutting off Southern supplies of salt and disrupting the local economy. Fortunately, Confederate spies had warned residents that the Yankees were on their way. There was plenty of time to prepare a hot reception.

In the meantime, Saltville literally emptied of occupants. The roads were crammed with refugees—horses, wagons, and slaves—all anticipating Burbridge's imminent arrival. Likewise, Abingdon was abandoned, except for some old men and boys.

Old Abraham Smith, who owned an interest in the Preston Salt Works, was an important plantation owner. As the result of good business and frugal saving, he had accumulated a rather large fortune for the time—$48,000 in gold and about $12,000 in jewels. Understandably, he was considerably worried that his valuables might fall into enemy hands.

Smith enlisted the help of his two sons, Eli and Samuel. Together they buried the old man's horde in the middle of a partially completed roadbed.

When Burbridge's troops appeared in Poor Valley on October 2, they were greeted by an assortment of soldiers, farmers, and laborers—all armed to the teeth. A pitched battle littered the valley with bodies.

In the meantime, Federal troopers, not actually engaged in the fighting, began blasting shut the caves from which salt was mined.

Abraham's son Eli was captured by the Yankees and was afraid of being hanged as a spy. He blurted out the story about the buried treasure, offering to tell the Yankees its location if they would spare his life and help him escape to Tennessee.

Sgt. Jack Harrington agreed to the plan. He, Eli, and Corporal Allen Brooks dug up the treasure and hid the cache in nearby Harmon's Cave. Then the good sergeant drew down on the unfortunate Eli and shot him for allegedly trying to escape. Harrington rejoined his troopers who were busily blasting shut the mouths of other caves that dotted the valley. A few minutes later the double-crossing sergeant himself was killed by a premature explosion.

By this time, the Yankees had had enough. Burbridge's 5,000 Federal troopers were no match for General John S. Williams's 3,000 inexperienced, yet determined, Southerners. Burbridge retreated through the Cumberland Gap and back into Kentucky from whence he had come.

Union casualties were high. Federals left about 350 soldiers on the field—about half of them Negro. The Confederate tally was only eight killed and 51 wounded—absolutely no doubt about who won the battle.

There was no sign of Eli among the dead or wounded. Abraham Smith and his son Samuel thought that he might have been captured by the Yankees and carted away as a prisoner of war. When father and son attempted to retrieve the treasure, *they found that missing too!* The shock of losing his son and his fortune—all on the same day—was just too much for the old man, and he died a short time after.

A few years later, a letter addressed to Abraham Smith was received by Samuel. The message, from former Union Corporal Allen Brooks, outlined the events that had taken place during the battle. Brooks admitted he was with Harrington when he dug up the treasure and that the sergeant had shot Eli, but the corporal insisted that he was only following orders. He had kept the secret to himself all these years. But on his deathbed, he felt he must confess to put his conscience at rest.

Brooks wrote that he and Sgt. Harrington had hidden the stolen loot in "a saltpeter cave, about a quarter of a mile distant from the little town church.... I had planned to return to Saltville and reveal the location of your money to you. But I am dying and I want you to know that I took no part in the murder of your son."

Samuel Smith tried to find the treasure on his own several times, but failed. Finally he gave up entirely and left the area. Since then, others have attempted to find the gold and jewels, but they, too, have failed.

W.C. Jameson, in his book **Buried Treasures of the Appalachians**, said the treasure lies buried in Harmon's Cave, located in Poor Valley between Allison's Gap and Saltville. And local tradition holds that the ghost of Abraham Smith guards his treasure jealously.

Whenever someone gets close to finding the gold and jewels, old Abraham moves his stash to another part of the cave. And apparently the old man is quite efficient in playing his ghostly game of hide and seek.

So far, no one has even gotten a "smell" of the treasure.

The Creature in the Barn

An old barn in Wise County is said to house a horrible creature that attacks and slashes intruders with its six-inch claws. But I'm not going to tell you where the barn is located. The farmer who owns the land is not interested in additional visitors. Too many people know the location of the barn already. And, according to him, there's a good chance someone is liable to get killed there!

The barn has stood at least 50 years. It might even stand 50 more. The weathered siding might appear to cling tenuously to upright oak frames, but the basic structure is sound. The farmer who owns the barn has considered burning the building to rid himself of the horror he claims lurks within but, so far, has failed to do so.

Presently the barn is unused. The owner admits he's afraid to go inside these days, especially after dark. But since I was with him (whatever that was worth), he consented to show me the inside of the building.

Having been raised on a farm, I saw the barn wasn't unusual—at least, not as far as barns go. The only thing odd was that the inside was devoid of anything—machinery, hay, straw, feed sacks, livestock—*anything* to indicate the building served a useful purpose.

"I tell you that something horrible lives in here," he said. "I got a glimpse of it once and I never, ever, want to see it again!"

Then my friend pointed to the floor. The wood in one place looked like it had been splintered and pushed up from underneath. Beneath, a deep hole gaped. "That's where the danged thing came out the first time," the farmer said.

The farmer thinks the creature lives underground—like some sort of impossible mole. Then at night it slithers out of its hole, searching for victims.

My friend said the monster first appeared six years ago. "I was in the barn late one night, rearranging bales of hay. I heard a noise, just like nails being pulled out of a board by a claw hammer. I looked out over the edge of the haystack but saw nothing."

The only light in the barn came from a single lantern hanging on the wall, my friend continued. Most of the interior was in shadow. He peered cautiously into the darkness. There it was again—that sound!

The farmer took the lantern from the wall and held it aloft. Once again, his keen eyes searched the dark interior of the barn. Nothing.

"A coon," he said to himself. Raccoons were always getting into his barn and making mischief. He returned the lantern to the hook on the wall and continued his work.

A few minutes later, the farmer heard another noise—this time coming from the hayloft where he was working. He turned just in time to see a black, glistening creature lunge across the hay bales and take a swing at him with long, sharp claws. The farmer turned to protect himself and felt a searing pain across his back. Then he was knocked down.

"I must have been knocked out," he remembered, "because when I finally opened my eyes, it was morning. My shirt was bloody and my back felt like a carved Thanksgiving turkey.

"The doctor said I must have tangled with a bear, but I don't think so. I think what attacked me was something else—much worse than any bear!"

My friend said he got only a glimpse of the creature, but he said it didn't *look* like a bear.

"It was low and squat. The eyes were huge and staring—something like a fish. And those claws were immense!"

Then the farmer said, "I want to show you something." With that he pulled off his shirt and showed me his back. Running across diagonally were three angry scars that looked just like claw marks.

"I don't know why the thing didn't finish me off while I was lying there unconscious," he said. "I must have been out for a couple hours, at least."

Two days after the incident, word of the farmer's encounter with the strange creature spread throughout the neighborhood. Of course, few people believed him. But that didn't stop neighbors from investigating the barn personally—especially the teenagers.

"It was all I could do to keep them away. I even called the law, but they couldn't spend all their time trying to keep people away from my barn."

Late one night, three teenagers finally crept into the barn. No one knows what happened, but since then no other young people have tried to find the creature.

"It was really odd. They wouldn't talk about what happened. But they must have told someone, because there were no more trespassers after that.

"I think they must have seen the same thing that I did and warned the others to stay away."

The Peeping Tom

There was once an old man who lived beside the Clinch River in a little cabin hidden by a dense tangle of thicket. Toward the end of his life, he became a hermit because he disliked people and their ways.

Ol' Sam, as he was called, was a veteran of The War Between The States. He fought in major battles including Gettysburg and Cold Harbor. Wounded once, his leg was amputated and he was forced to hobble around on a crutch for the rest of his life.

Sam never married. Instead he kept to himself on a little plot of land he bought before the war. He never married nor had any children.

By the turn of the century, Sam was nearly 70. Grizzled and unkempt, he shunned his neighbors and they shunned him. Some folks even thought Sam was in league with the devil. Rumor was that Sam roamed around in the middle of the night, peering in the windows of townsfolk.

One night a young woman was preparing for bed when she heard a noise outside her window. The woman turned just in time to see the grizzled face of Ol' Sam leering at her through the glass. She screamed, but by the time her father ran outside to catch the culprit, he was gone.

"Who was it?" the father asked his daughter.

"Ol' Sam," the daughter sputtered, thoroughly frightened. "Ol' Sam stood outside the window, staring at me! And he had this horrible grin on his face!"

The next day the young woman's father visited the sheriff and reported the incident.

"I can't figure this out," the sheriff said, scratching his head. "Is your daughter *sure* it was Ol' Sam she saw last night?"

"Absolutely, Sheriff. She seen him clearly through the window."

"But her bedroom is on the second floor of your house, ain't it?"

"Yes sir."

"Then, just how do you figure he climbed all the way up there with just one leg, then ran away so fast when you went after him?"

The farmer was getting frustrated with all the talk. "I don't know, Sheriff," he replied sharply. "I just know my daughter doesn't lie. Now, why don't you go out there to that cabin of his and arrest him?"

"Can't rightly do that," the sheriff answered. "Sam's down at John Tasker's."

The farmer's eyebrows nearly lifted off his face in surprise. "What in the blazes is he doin' down there workin' for the undertaker?"

"He ain't," the sheriff answered darkly. "Ol' Sam died yesterday morning."

Campground Ghosts

This is a true story told to me by John and Maureen Stanton of Knoxville, Tennessee—a classic tale if I ever heard one!

Throughout Southwest Virginia are favored places where parties of Indians camped for the night. For modern relic hunters, these spots are gold mines of artifacts—arrowheads, tools, etc. For ghost hunters, they are often places where spirits of the dead are encountered. In Southwest Virginia alone, there must be thousands of ghost stories centering around these ancient campgrounds of the Cherokee.

One such campground is located beside the Clinch River in Wise County. It was here that a couple, trying to put romance back in their lives with a moonlight stroll, unexpectedly encountered shadows of the past—realistic specters of long-dead Native Americans.

John and Maureen Stanton of Knoxville were recently in St. Paul, visiting relatives whom they hadn't seen in quite a while. The house, a Swiss chalet, was located just a few yards from the Clinch, nestled in a lush patch of woods and tangled over in rhododendron. All in all, the house was in an idyllic setting for the rekindling of romance.

Married over 30 years, John and Maureen Stanton's three children had married and left home, the last in early spring. Middle-aged and not having to worry about pediatrician visits and PTA meetings or waiting up until all hours of the night for their daughters to return from dates, the Stantons hardly knew what to do with themselves. John, especially, had become sullen and short-tempered in recent months.

When first married, the Stantons decided to wait a few years before having children. Memories of those early days were filled with fun and romance. Then the first daughter arrived, and the couple got down to the serious job of parenting. There were two more girls and, for the next 20 years or so, the couple thought only of their children. And when the last of them married and set up her own home, the Stantons realized how much their lives had been controlled by the wants and needs of their children—and how they were lost without them.

The couple realized there was something terribly wrong with their relationship. These few days away from Knoxville would be a godsend.

"I have an idea," Maureen told her husband on the last day of their visit. "Let's go out tonight, after it gets dark, and explore the riverbank by moonlight."

John agreed that it might be a good idea. At least, it was a romantic notion, and their marriage desperately needed a little more romance in it.

Their host agreed. The Clinch was, indeed, beautiful by moonlight, and tonight promised to be a perfect night.

"We'd accompany you ourselves," he said, "but I promised my wife I'd help her out tonight."

"Which way should we go," John asked. "It's been a long time since I was a Boy Scout, and I don't want to get the both of us lost."

"The path by the river is well-worn. Keep to that and you won't get lost."

After a good supper and amiable conversation afterwards, topped off by a comforting wine, their host said, "Be careful. There are ghosts of Indians out there in the forest. Be sure they don't get you."

The couple laughed. "You've got to be kidding," John said. "Ghosts?"

"Don't laugh. There used to be an old Indian campground down by the river, just a little way from here. The local legend is that sometimes, in the dark of the night, the ghosts of Indians will appear around a campfire. I know a number of people who say they've actually seen them."

"I don't believe in ghosts," John said.

"Well," their host laughed, "have it your way. But don't say I didn't warn you."

The night was a bit chilly, even though it was the middle of August. The couple wrapped themselves up against the night air and walked, hand in hand, toward the river.

The Clinch that night was beautiful. The moon was out in full bloom, and its golden beams played on the rippling surface of the water. The couple walked along the edge of the river, through the woods. About 600 yards from the house, they smelled wood smoke.

"Campers must be in the woods," Maureen told her husband. "It's a good night for it."

"I think we'd better be careful," John warned. "We don't know who those people are."

"Let's find out," his adventurous wife said. "Maybe it's a bunch of kids. I remember we used to camp out all the time."

The pair crept quietly through the underbrush until they came to a little clearing. In the center was a fire. Maureen gasped. Sitting around the blaze, in a circle, were a half dozen half-naked Indians.

"This can't be," John whispered to his wife.

"Are they the ghosts we were told about?" his wife asked anxiously.

"Boy Scouts," her husband answered. "They have to be Boy Scouts. We used to do things like that when we camped—dress up like Indians and tell stories."

"I think these people are a little old to be Boy Scouts," Maureen observed dryly.

Indeed, these were full-grown men. One or two of them looked to be in their 40s. All had long black hair; all wore a breechcloth or buckskins. Bows, arrows, and spears lay on the ground beside them.

"I don't believe in ghosts!" John reassured himself.

Maureen was getting excited. She had always been interested in the supernatural. She had read every book she could find on the subject. But she had never seen a ghost. Now there were six of them right in front of her eyes. It was almost too good to be true!

"I think we'd better go back to the house," John whispered nervously. "I don't like this."

"No. Let's get closer. Ghosts can't hurt you. See if you can hear what they're saying."

They moved a few more steps closer, their ears alert for the slightest sound. Soon they heard murmuring. The pair crouched behind a sprawling rhododendron bush.

"Can you make it out?" Maureen whispered to her husband. "Can you hear what they're saying?"

"Sounds like gibberish," her husband replied. "Some kind of Indian language, I suspect."

Maureen was more excited than ever. "Darn. We need to get closer."

"I still think we need to get out of here—back to the house."

Suddenly a twig snapped behind them. They nearly jumped out of their skins.

"BOO!!!"

The startled couple wheeled around. Standing behind them was their grinning host. Then there was the sound of more laughter. John turned toward the campfire and saw the "Indians" getting up and walking toward them.

"Well," the host said. "What do you think of my Indians?"

"A trick," Maureen hissed. "This was nothing but a dirty trick."

"Not really. In fact, this was more of a test. I'm sorry you had to be the guinea pigs, but the opportunity was too good to pass up."

John felt his blood rush to his face. "Just what do you mean, 'a test'?"

"Well," his host began, "you've heard about Civil War reenactment groups. They get up in uniforms and play soldier on weekends. This is kind of the same thing—sort of. We're starting an Indian reenactment group."

"What for?"

"Pageants, plays and things like that."

John looked around him. They *were* surrounded by *rather authentic looking Indians*. Not a bad job, for white men.

"You see, John, we had to test out our costumes on someone. When you two said you wanted to take a midnight stroll along the river tonight, I saw a chance I couldn't pass up. So I called the boys and we set this whole thing up for your benefit, as well as ours. I hope you're not too mad at us."

Then it was John's turn to laugh. The joke had been on him and Maureen—and a pretty good joke, too.

"I'll have to give it to you," John said. "You sure fooled us. But you're still not as authentic as you would like to think you are. There's still something wrong with your total performance."

The host raised his eyebrows. "What's that?"

John pointed to the fire. "That," he said. "Real Indians wouldn't leave their fire unattended and set the woods ablaze."

John was right. Some of the undergrowth was now alight. With a startled yelp, the "Indians" rushed towards the spreading campfire and started beating the flames with sticks and even their bare hands. When John and Maureen watched the "Indians" jumping around in a panic, both started laughing hysterically.

"What would old Hiawatha say about this?" John wondered out loud.

The Mystery of Old Rupp

The following tale can rightfully be classified as a "Horror Tale from Lovers' Lane." These are time-honored stories, told by young men to their female companions, while parked in secluded areas at night. These stories have a rich tradition, and hundreds—maybe even thousands—of them exist in all parts of the country. But I have never encountered another story like this one and include it here as one of my favorites of the genre.

What satanic creature stalks the woods and fields near Big Stone Gap in Wise County? Some folks claim it's a genuine Old World vampire, an unholy fiend of the night that thirsts for human blood. Others say the creature is very much human—a demented cannibal with an insatiable appetite for human flesh.

Either way, the creature is not something a person would want to meet alone on a dark night!

Bizarre and mysterious deaths—both animal and human—have been reported in the area, some dating back to the turn of the twentieth century. All are blamed on the monster.

Worse yet, this horrific creature may still, even today, search the countryside for victims.

Big Stone Gap, located at the point where the Powell River rushes through a water gap in Stone Mountain, was a boom town in the final years of the nineteenth century. As early as 1881, a steam-powered sawmill was brought into town and houses began going up. Trains of the

South Atlantic & Ohio and the Louisville & Nashville Railroads reached the town in the early part of 1891. The boom was on!

Not even the wide-open towns of the Yukon during the Alaska gold rush could compare to it. New speculators arrived every day, in every conceivable mode of transportation. Novelist John Fox, Jr., wrote of the town in *Back Home* magazine in colorful, descriptive prose:

"Horses and mules were drowned in the mudholes along the roads, such were the floods. The incomers slept eight in a room, burned oil at a dollar a gallon, and ate potatoes at ten cents apiece.... Men bought [town lots] for thirty dollars apiece and sold them for a thousand. They had the world in a sling and if they wished could toss it playfully to the sun and it would drop back into their hands again."

While it lasted, Big Stone Gap's flirtation with glorious prosperity was wild and freewheeling. The town attracted thousands, including some recent immigrants to America. One was a man named Rupp, a tall, dark European with a vague and mysterious background.

Rupp built a small cabin on the outskirts of town and promptly became a recluse. No one saw him enter or leave the cabin, nor even appear in town, so they assumed he remained indoors at all times.

"A very odd character," the townsfolk agreed. But they were much too busy with their own enterprises to give the matter much more than a passing thought.

That is, until their cattle began to be slaughtered.

One farmer lost two prize cows in a single night. Both had been dismembered and drained of blood! Only the head and hindquarters of each animal remained in the field.

The natural assumption was that a wild animal—a bear or a wolf— was the culprit. But wolves and bears don't suck the blood from an animal. The veins in these slain creatures were as innocent of blood as a butchered hog!

When townsfolk looked around for an explanation, and no logical one was forthcoming, superstition took over and suspicion fell upon the mysterious Rupp.

Then the local population shivered in horror when a couple of local boys reported something they had seen in Rupp's cabin late one night.

Rupp, like all odd people, was often the target of juvenile pranksters. When neighborhood youths weren't tormenting him by throwing rocks at his door, they were peering in his windows. This pair was in the process of the latter when they saw something that made their blood run cold.

Rupp was sitting by his fireplace, they said, eating what appeared to be a large piece of *raw meat*. It looked very much like the front leg of a cow! When Rupp turned and saw the astonished boys looking in through the glass, he quickly hid his dinner. Then he ran outside and chased the boys into the forest.

"What kind of maniac eats raw meat when he is perfectly capable of building a fire and cooking his meal over it?" some of the townsfolk asked themselves.

But the sheriff was not so easily convinced the law had been broken, especially by Rupp. No one had seen him kill the cattle or the sheep which had also recently turned up dead and mutilated. This was the twentieth century, and the Home Guard had been disbanded. Reason prevailed in Big Stone Gap.

In the past the Home Guard had kept the peace in Big Stone Gap. These were honorable men, armed to the teeth, working under the sanction of the court in the absence of an official police force. On occasion, the Home Guard was even called out to watch a special prisoner.

The Home Guard's membership boasted a who's who of the leading citizens of Big Stone Gap, including John Fox, Jr., author of the novel **Trail of the Lonesome Pine**. At the blast of one of their ever-present whistles, men would instantly gather to keep the peace. But now, as Big Stone Gap matured, there was no longer use for the Guard or their methods.

"There's no law against a fella eating what he wants to," the sheriff told the group of citizens that had come to see him about Rupp. "I can't go out there and arrest Mr. Rupp for eating raw meat, just on the say-so of these-here boys."

Two weeks later, the town drunk disappeared. The sheriff asked around Big Stone Gap. Had anybody seen him? No, they had not.

A few days afterwards the man was found in the woods, his body drained of blood—just like the cattle. Furthermore, there was an arm and a leg missing from the body. Someone pointed out the fact that Rupp's cabin was only a quarter mile from the murder spot.

Still, the sheriff refused to arrest Rupp or even question him about what appeared to be an unsolved murder. It took another brutal killing before the sheriff sprang to action.

This time, the murdered man was a traveling salesman who had just finished a two-day stay in Big Stone Gap. His body was also found in the woods, a short distance from Rupp's cabin. It, too, was missing several limbs, and the body was drained of blood.

"Now maybe you'll do something, Sheriff," the angry townspeople shouted.

"Reckon I better had," the sheriff replied.

An hour later the sheriff set out for Rupp's cabin; that was the last time anybody saw him!

By this time, the townspeople were not only angry, but terrified at a series of murders and mutilations they could not solve. But they were sure of the perpetrator. They formed a vigilante posse and determined to go out to Rupp's cabin in force.

Just after dark, about a dozen people assembled just outside the town, torches in hand, a murderous intent at the ready.

Most of the townsfolk had decided they were dealing with a cannibal. Scotsmen in the group already knew the Old World legend of Sawney Bean and his infamous family—cannibals all. They had convinced the rest of the posse that this might be the case with Rupp. The mysterious, dark, sinister foreigner might actually have a craving to eat human flesh, just like Sawney. In fact, he might even be kin to Sawney himself.

Sawney, his wife, and his children lived in a cave in County Galloway during the reign of James I. From their secluded hideaway they set upon travelers, murdering them for their gold. Then they dragged the bodies back to the cave, quartered them, and preserved the parts in brine, which they consumed at their leisure.

This went on for 20 years or more. No one could quite figure out where the travelers were disappearing to, nor their fate when they got there. Understandably, there was panic in the countryside. Several innocent people were accused of the crimes and hanged. But Sawney and his family remained undetected in their cave. They inbred with each other, and insanity flourished among them. And all became cannibals, just like their patriarch.

After a generation or so, the family had grown considerably and consisted of Sawney, his wife, eight sons, six daughters, 18 grandsons, and

14 granddaughters.

Finally, one of Sawney's intended victims escaped—the first to ever do so. When he returned to Glasgow and told the authorities what had happened, the king himself decided to ride out with 400 men and rid the countryside of the menace.

After a long search, bloodhounds found the Beans' cave, which was then attacked by the king's men. All of Bean's tribe was captured, brought back to Leith, and pinioned. Evidence found in the cave confirmed suspicions of devilish goings-on, and the next day Sawney and his entire family were burned at the stake.

Could the mysterious Rupp be another Sawney Bean? The townspeople were taking no chances. They were well-armed and loaded for bear. And they were determined to confront the monster at his own door.

When they arrived at Rupp's cabin, a light was burning in the window. Two or three men cautiously approached the front door. The others, their torches now extinguished, hid in the undergrowth surrounding the cabin.

One of the men carefully tested the front door. He jumped back in surprise as it creaked open. The men at the door charged into the cabin while the others jumped from their hiding places and rushed forward.

Inside the cabin was a scene of horror. Body parts littered the floor. The smell was overpowering. The men ran outside, coughing and gagging.

Rupp was gone. When members of the posse recovered their wits (as well as their stomachs), they searched the surrounding woods. Nothing. Rupp had totally disappeared.

The men then set the cabin afire. They were determined nothing would be left of the grisly interior after the flames had done their work.

The posse stood around the blazing cabin in a circle, yellow firelight reflected in their faces. By the time the cabin had collapsed upon itself and was reduced to a blazing, shapeless heap, most of the party had returned to town, leaving only a few men to make sure the fire didn't spread to the woods.

Tomorrow they would conduct a thorough search of the countryside and capture the monster who had committed the grisly murders. But a week later, Rupp was still missing.

He was never seen again.

Since that time there has been much speculation about what happened to the mysterious Rupp. Some say he fled into the woods, just before the posse reached his house. Some say he escaped through a trapdoor in the floor.

One report said that Rupp somehow made his way back to Europe, where he lived to be a very old man and died in obscurity.

But some contend that Rupp still roams the woods near Big Stone Gap, especially on nights when the moon is full, where couples are parked on lonely roads; and his stomach is empty.

A Very Sensitive Child

There's always a sense of poignancy when a house is haunted by the ghost of a child. Who are these little ones and how did they die? Ghostly children, especially, try to reach out to the living for companionship. Here is a tale from Wise County that illustrates the sad, lonely side of the supernatural.

Part of Hurricane Road, in the city of Wise, runs parallel to a small creek. On the other side of the creek is a row of houses, each with its own driveway bridge spanning the water.

On the surface, this middle-class residential area doesn't look as if it would attract spirits. Certainly, the houses do not fit the image of being haunted. But one of the houses, a one-story brick affair, is the home of the ghost of a playful little girl.

Those familiar with her antics say she loves being around people, unless they upset her or make her sad. And if she likes the current tenants, she adopts them and becomes part of their family, whether they like it or not.

In October 1992, a new tenant moved into the house. She had children of her own—two boys aged eight and ten. She also had two friends with whom she spent a lot of time.

One friend was Keith Snodgrass of Big Stone Gap. The other was Michelle Jones. Both attended Mountain Empire Community College in Big Stone Gap. Both were students of folklorist Ramond Burgin and were quite familiar with local ghost tales.

And both said they have seen the ghost of the little girl on more than one occasion.

The new tenant first suspected something odd about the house when her boys reported a new playmate. They were in the front yard when they were approached by a little girl of six or seven, oddly dressed in a nightgown. She stayed with the boys for awhile, then disappeared.

"The boys didn't recognize her as a ghost," Michelle Jones said. "But they told their mother about the strange meeting anyway."

The mother asked around the neighborhood, but no little girl fitting the description lived there. Then one of the neighbors told her that a ghost lived in her house.

"The ghost obviously likes to be around people," Jones said. "She's quite a normal little girl—mischievous. She likes to run through the house and knock things out of place."

Apparently the ghost is not malevolent, but that doesn't mean that experiences with her are not unnerving. Keith Snodgrass shudders when he tells about both of his brushes with her.

"I was sitting at the table one night when the refrigerator door opened and closed by itself," he said. "Then I heard little footsteps running down the hall and the sound of a child giggling."

A few minutes later Snodgrass, himself, got up, opened the refrigerator door, got something to eat, and returned to the table. Once again, the refrigerator door opened all by itself.

"I saw a six- or seven-year-old girl in a nightgown holding the door," he said. She had long hair, blue eyes, and was staring at me with a mischievous grin on her face. She was also transparent. I screamed and she disappeared."

A few days later, Snodgrass, Jones, and two others had spent the better part of an evening playing Uno in the living room. Snodgrass became thirsty about 12:30 a.m. and decided to get something to drink. He walked down the hall on his way to the kitchen.

Suddenly, the ghost burst from the kitchen and ran up the hall. Snodgrass's hair stood up on the back of his neck, and he felt what he described as a cold wind while the ghost ran right through him.

Once again, he screamed.

While shaking up the living with unexpected appearances and ghostly high jinks, the little girl also has a poignant side—an element of sadness.

It must be very lonely for her in her world.

"I was leaving the house one night to attend a play rehearsal," Michelle Jones began. "Walking to the car, I looked back to the house and saw a little girl at the window. Her hands and face were pressed up against the glass. The child's expression was unclear, but I got the message she didn't want me to leave her alone, or that she was sad I was leaving.

"I turned to tell someone that I had seen her, and when I turned around again, she was gone."

For nearly two months, the ghost of the little girl made her presence known in the house. Then one day, something happened to change all that.

"The ghost tends to adopt anyone living in the house," Jones said, "especially females. And she wants them to be happy.

"One day, my friend had a very loud argument with her mother over the telephone. That was just before Thanksgiving. And after that, we never heard from the ghost again.

"I think the argument upset the little ghost the same way it might upset a normal child. I don't think she likes bad feelings."

In January 1993, the house became vacant again. Is the ghost of the little girl still there? Probably. But the next tenants need to watch their tone of voice. Their ghost is not one who enjoys emotional trauma.

It seems as if they will be dealing with a very sensitive child.

The Black Dog of Coeburn

Coeburn, in Wise County, is right in the middle of coal mining country. Surrounded by rugged mountains, the area has more than its share of deep hollows—dark, eerie places where the sun seldom reaches. In one of these narrow slashes between mountains is said to be a tumbledown log cabin, neglected by time and ravaged by the elements. Tradition holds that this cabin was once the home of an evil witch so powerful that anyone encountering her would be put under an irrevocable spell.

Today the hollow is still shunned because it is believed to be haunted. A mysterious phantom dog still roams the depths, wailing mournfully, as if in agony. The dog is also claimed to be the evil end of one of the witch's most hideous spells.

The story begins 100 years ago when Coeburn contained no more than a few isolated houses, but it did contain a lot of promise. In 1891, three years before the town was finally incorporated, the first passenger train of the Norfolk & Western Railway chugged into Coeburn. The train's arrival was so significant to the progress of Coeburn that the entire community, dressed to the nines, appeared at the station to greet the train.

One of the first passengers to disembark was a man named Ledford. He was a friend of Tom Hurd, who would later become the first Sergeant (sheriff) of Coeburn.

Ledford was a land developer and mining engineer who wanted to survey tracts of land around town for possible mining operations. He hired a horse and a laborer to carry his gear, and he was soon spending days at a time traipsing up and down the mountains and exploring dark hollows, searching for telltale signs of coal. At least twice a week he returned to Coeburn for rest and relaxation.

One night, sitting in a local tavern, some of the men told Ledford about the haunted hollow and the witch who lived there. Ledford had recently been to the head of the hollow. He had come back that afternoon, excited that he had found signs of coal there. The local men immediately recognized the hollow he described and began to warn him about ever going there again. And they told him about the witch.

"I hear that old woman can cast some right powerful spells," one of the men told him. "Most people hereabouts are scared even to get within sight of her cabin. They're afraid she might do something to them."

Ledford laughed. "I'm not superstitious," he said. "I don't believe in witches. I'm going up there in a few days to see whether I can buy some of her land from her. I'll give her a good price. My company will even build her another house if she wants."

Another man shook his head. "She'll never sell," he said. "And you'll be sorry you ever went up there in the first place. She'll hex you for sure."

But Ledford wasn't listening. He was so excited about his find that all he thought of were profits.

The next day, as he was loading his horses and preparing to leave for the hollow, his hired man announced that he wasn't going. No amount of argument could convince him otherwise. So Ledford set off alone, angry and muttering to himself about superstitious natives.

A week later, Ledford had not returned to town. A group of the men, armed to the teeth, decided to look for him. They planned to go to the head of the haunted hollow, but no farther.

When they arrived at their destination two hours later, they peered into the darkness to see if they could see any sign of Ledford. They saw nothing.

It was about 6:00 in the evening, and it was beginning to get dark. The last rays of the sun had just touched the top of the mountains when they heard a low, mournful howl coming from the hollow. The men looked at each other fearfully.

"What was that?" one of them asked.

Just then another pointed into the darkness and said, "Look."

A pair of glowing red eyes, about two feet off the ground, stared at them from among the trees. Cold chills went down the backs of the search party, and the short hair on the back of their necks stood straight up. The eyes stared at them, unblinking.

"Ledford? Is that you?" one of the men asked, though he didn't quite know why.

Another howl—then a low, rumbling voice came from the trees. "Go back," the voice said.

"Where are you, Ledford. We're here to help."

"I said, 'Go back,' " the voice repeated. "There is danger here."

Another low howl cut through the silence of the evening. The eyes began to move away. The sound of brush being trampled underfoot was heard in the hollow.

Suddenly, one of the men pointed. "Look!" he exclaimed as he shivered in fear.

Silhouetted against the darkening trees was the form of a large black dog. It stopped and turned toward the men, its flashing eyes glowing red in the darkness. Then it opened its mouth and in a rumbling voice said, "I *was* Ledford. And if you venture any further, you will be as I am now. My mistress is nigh and searches for more pets to play with."

Then a high-pitched, screaming laugh tore through the woods. The search party had had enough. They ran back to Coeburn as fast as their legs could carry them.

Ever since that day, no one has had the desire to go near the haunted hollow again.

According to popular legend, the devil often manifests himself in the form of a black dog. Likewise, witches often have black animals (called "familiars") for companions. The black dog is central to these tales. Superstition is also linked with the howling of a dog.

There is a Celtic superstition that a howling dog is symbolic of the wind god who summons up the spirit of death. According to Claudia de Lys, "Many think, even today, that the howling of the dog is provoked by the apparition of Death itself, invisible to man, but seen or sensed by animals, especially the dog. It is also believed that a wraith or specter in the exact likeness of a living person appears just before death comes, and can be seen by the dog, causing it to bellow forth these sinister sounds."

Memories of Rye Cove

On May 2, 1929, one of the most tragic events in the history of Southwest Virginia befell the little town of Rye Cove in Scott County.

Students were just settling down to another day in Rye Cove Schoolhouse. Suddenly, the southwest sky got dark. An unnatural wind whipped up dust devils on nearby streets.

Then it hit. A tornado of gigantic proportions slammed into the wooden school.

The sudden vacuum created by the funnel blew out windows. Then timbers snapped and flew around like matchsticks.

Screams of students and teachers—and the roar of death—filled the air.

Suddenly, the entire school was lifted off its foundation and slammed back to earth. Bodies were hurled through the air. Shards of glass swirled around like leaves in an autumn gale. Desks, books, and spears of shattered wood flew through the air like deadly missiles.

Then all was quiet.

At first, students were so stunned they didn't know what to do. Many were buried under mounds of debris. Some were injured. Others were dead.

One girl had a one by six wooden plank driven clean through her body. Another student had been almost decapitated by flying glass.

A student cried out for help. Another was crying softly, slowly slipping into shock. One by one, the students picked themselves up, as broken timbers slid off their backs and crashed to the ground in choking clouds of plaster dust.

"Children, come outside," one of the teachers was heard to say. How ironic. There was no roof on the building. They *were* outside.

Help soon arrived. Men from the community were soon picking through the wreckage, looking for survivors.

The injured were taken to King's Mountain Memorial Hospital in Bristol. Kingsport Hospital admitted a few more. The Red Cross responded. Help came from Gate City, Kingsport, Bristol, and Johnson City.

But for the dead, nothing could be done. Thirteen people lost their lives that spring day—one teacher and 12 students.

Soon after, through the generosity of Mrs. W.D. Smith, a memorial plaque was erected naming those who lost their lives in the disaster. A song about the tragedy was even written, and it became a popular hit in the 1930s.

In that moment of death, time was apparently frozen forever. Since then, on May 2nd of each year—on the anniversary of the tornado—the phantom roar of a mighty wind gushes from a clear sky, and the ghostly cries of children are heard...

...and history repeats itself once more.

The Nocturnal Adventure
of Augustus F. Henderson

The human mind is capable of almost anything—we have yet to discover its full power. Certainly the brain is the seat of our awareness—our total consciousness is controlled by a three-pound mass of irregular gray tissue. But what about the unconscious? Can we control behavior when the conscious part of the brain is inactive? Let's explore that possibility with one of the wildest tales to come out of Southwest Virginia. The incident was originally divulged by "Aunt Sister Neel" and duly printed in the *Holston Methodist* newspaper many years ago. Historian Charles A. Johnson used the story verbatim in his <u>A Narrative History of Wise County, Virginia</u> originally published in 1938, reprinted by The Overmountain Press, in 1988. Johnson's version is the basis for my retelling of the story.

There was no doubt that Captain John W. Harmon was a solid citizen of Kimberlin Creek. It was also a well-known fact that Captain Harmon was one of the best hunters in the county—the amount of game in his smokehouse attested to that. His marksmanship—even with a smoothbore musket—was legendary—his pack of hunting dogs was regarded as the best in the area.

Captain Harmon lived a few miles from Kimberlin campground, famous for Methodist revivals and camp meetings. His nephew, with whom he lived at the time, was Augustus F. (Gus) Henderson, a recent graduate of Emory and Henry College who had just begun to read the law. Harmon's wife, Hester, was the daughter of a local preacher, David

Byrnes, and was a devout Christian. Both husband and wife enjoyed the campground revivals and attended them at every opportunity.

It was the duty of local women to cook and bake for revival guests. The night before a revival was to begin, Hester was thus occupied inside the house. About 10:00, Harmon walked into the kitchen. "Hester, while you're finishing up your work, I believe I'll go down to the big bottom and catch a coon. They're eating up all my corn."

Harmon had not gotten very far when his dogs flushed out a raccoon. The terrified animal made a beeline for a dead hickory tree that stood in the middle of the cornfield.

For a moment, Harmon considered cutting the tree down. But he decided it would destroy more corn in its fall than the coon could by stealing it.

Leaving the dogs at the bottom of the tree to keep the coon occupied, Harmon returned to the house and called to his wife to wake his nephew, give him a rifle, and send him down the hill to the tree.

Hester woke Gus who climbed out of bed, dressed, and took the gun, all without a word. Then he walked the half mile down the hill to the dead hickory where Harmon and his dogs stood, gazing up at the coon in the branches. Gus handed the gun to his uncle. Then without a word, he began climbing the tree.

"Stop," Harmon shouted to his nephew. "That tree is dead and it may break off with your weight!"

Gus continued climbing as if he hadn't heard a thing his uncle said to him.

"Don't go any farther," Harmon shouted again, but Gus continued up the hickory and rapidly approached the coon.

Harmon attempted to shoot the coon before Gus reached him, but it was too dark to get the animal in his sights. His only hope was to move around the tree and place the animal between him and the moon (mooning the coon) so he could squeeze off a clear shot. But before he could do this, Gus had gotten so near the cornered animal that it was dangerous to shoot.

"Get out of there," Harmon shouted again, but to no avail. Gus began shaking the branch on which the coon cowered. Finally the animal lost his foothold and dropped to the ground. In an instant the dogs were on him.

During the confusion, Harmon was occupied with the dogs and didn't notice Gus climbing out of the tree and disappearing back in the house. By the time he returned, Gus had gone back to his bed.

The next morning, Harmon was determined that he was going to bless out his nephew for the foolhardy trick he had pulled the night before. As they sat at breakfast, Harmon said:

"Gus, last night you must have lost your temper and what little sense you had. I was very much alarmed and looked every moment to see you killed. If you were a boy and not a full-grown man, I would take you to the barn and give you a regular lashing!"

Gus was totally dumfounded at his uncle. What had he done to deserve such a tongue lashing? So he did the most logical thing he could think of. He asked.

"The climbing of that dead tree last night in the middle of the corn-field," his uncle replied angrily. "The shaking down of that coon. I was there ready to shoot it!"

The nephew was even more amazed. "I climbed no tree," he protested, "and shook no coon. I retired at nine and slept soundly until Aunty called me to breakfast. If I did any of the things of which you accuse me, I was either disembodied or fast asleep!"

And he was right, the article continued. Gus had gotten out of bed, dressed, carried the gun half a mile to the field to his uncle, climbed the tree, shaken off the coon, returned home, undressed, and retired, all in his sleep.

According to The Oxford Companion to the Mind, somnambu-lism (or sleepwalking) is said to take place when the sleeper is not in dreaming (REM) sleep. Sleepwalking is most common in children but not unknown in adults. The tendency to sleepwalk may be inher-ited and run in families. During episodes of somnambulism, the sleeper may talk and walk, but he appears unresponsive to things going on around him. He avoids obstacles but may incur danger because he is clumsy. He may return to bed on his own, and he has no waking memory of the incident.

An Army of Ghosts

Civil War battles are sometimes major spawning grounds of ghostly tales. In fact, conflict and trauma seem to affect the existence of the supernatural. Ghost armies clash, often on the anniversaries of the battles in which they participated.

At Gettysburg, Pennsylvania, for example, it is said that each July 3 the ground between Seminary and Cemetery Ridges rings with the sound of cannon and musketfire, punctuated by the anguished cries of the wounded. On that day, in 1863, General George Pickett flung 30,000 of his Southerners against the well-entrenched Federals, dug in on Cemetery Ridge. He marched his troops in close-order formation over $1^1/4$ miles of open field into murderous Federal fire. As a result, only a third of his men survived the battle that has become known as "Pickett's Charge."

Poor Valley, near Saltville, was the scene of another major Civil War battle when Union General Burbridge invaded in October 1864 with 5,000 troops.

Burbridge's orders were to destroy the salt mines in and around Saltville, thereby cutting off Southern supplies of salt and disrupting the local economy. About 350 Federals died—but only eight Confederates—in an extremely lopsided battle. While Federal troops were occupied blowing up mines, Confederate sharpshooters were busily blasting Yankees into eternity.

Many of the Federal troops were black. Just recently, the Union had begun trusting freed slaves and free Negroes to wear Army blue, but always under the watchful eye of a white officer. During the battle of Saltville, these black soldiers more than distinguished themselves in the assault of Dibrell's Brigade on October 2nd.

After a massive charge, Dibrell's men fell back to the west side of Cedar Creek in disarray. Then, suddenly, Dibrell's forces regrouped and attacked, wading into the Federals, inflicting horrendous casualties.

The fighting went on for some time, and by the time the shooting died down, the rich ground of poor valley was littered with Union dead. Soundly defeated, Burbridge limped back through the Cumberland Gap and returned to Kentucky.

The battle of Saltville was a traumatic event for both armies, though the South lost only eight men (51 were wounded) in the fight. But echoes of that terrible battle persist to the present day.

Legend says that every October, if a person is quiet and listens very carefully, he can still hear the roar of the cannon and the cries of the wounded—audible shadows, over 120 years old, the ghosts of one of the greatest battles ever fought on Southwest Virginia ground.

The Unquiet Grave

In Tazewell County there is a family burial plot located high on a windy hill, the kind of place where all properly haunted graveyards should be located.

The graveyard is nearly 200 years old. Descendants of the original settlers still keep the place cleared of brush and weeds. Occasionally, a family member is still buried there, but not very often.

One of the graves causes the caretakers problems, not to mention a healthy case of the willies. "None of us can figure it out," one of the family told me recently. "I don't know how many times we've tried to fill in that damned hole. One time we even tried concrete. But you come back the next day, and it looks as if someone has been digging it out again. The funny thing about it, the hole doesn't look like it's being shoveled out from the top or has collapsed in from the bottom. Rather, it looks like something has tried to tunnel out from underneath!"

"Could it be a mole or ground hog?" I asked.

"Possibly," the man answered. "But it has to be the biggest varmint in these parts. That hole must be at least 18 inches across."

According to the marker, and family lore, the grave belongs to a young woman who died tragically—although there are no records to indicate just how she died. The elements have even erased her name from the stone marker.

One time a couple of boys decided to sit up in the graveyard all night to see for themselves what was digging the hole. Earlier in the day the caretaker had just filled in the opening for the umpteenth time. Now, just after nightfall, the boys settled down behind some nearby vines. They had brought a shotgun with them, hoping to shoot the animal responsible for digging out the grave.

Around 11:00 p.m. they heard a scratching noise. They craned their necks, peering into the blackness. The noise seemed to be coming from the general direction of the grave.

One of the boys stood up and parted the vines so he could see better. "Anything?" the other boy asked.

"Not yet," he answered. "Hand me the gun. I want to be ready."

Suddenly the scratching stopped. All was silent except for the sound of a few crickets chirping by a little stream nearby. The second boy carefully rose up and peered through the vines.

"Can't see a blamed thing," he whispered to the other.

Then a white mist began rising from the grave. The boys' eyes became as wide as saucers. Slowly the mist swirled and shaped itself into what looked like a human torso—a young girl. Both boys were shaking so much that their teeth clacked.

The form began to drift leisurely off into the field. As soon as it disappeared, the two boys scrambled to their feet and hightailed it back home, afraid to come out for the rest of the night.

They never returned to the graveyard after the experience—at least, not after dark.

"I don't know if I believe the story or not," my friend said, a funny look in his eyes. "That happened quite a few years ago. I've heard of haunts rising in graveyards before, but I've never seen any myself.

"But you can't deny the fact that grave won't stay shut, and we've never seen an animal out there. There has to be some kind of explanation for all this."

"Have you ever come out here yourself after dark and watched?" I asked.

"No! And I don't aim to, neither."

Lore of the unquiet grave permeates East Tennessee and Southwest Virginia folklore. There is even an old Scotch-Irish ballad called "The Unquiet Grave," still sung by older folks. It tells the story of a troubled ghost who longs for rest.

In the past, our ancestors took elaborate precautions to prevent spirits from rising out of graves to torment the living. From the time a person died until burial, the mourners raced against time with the devil. Until the departed was safely underground, our ancestors believed there was a chance the minions of hell would snatch away the soul. If that happened, a restless spirit resulted.

One way to prevent this was to sit up with the body. It was believed that watching the corpse would prevent its soul from being whisked away by the devil.

Then, too, there was the problem of suicides. These bodies could not be buried in consecrated ground because anyone taking his own life had committed an unforgivable sin.

Suicides were buried at crossroads, with a wooden stake driven through the heart to prevent undesired resurrections. A cross was sometimes laid on the chest as an added precaution.

If the boys really did see a ghost that night in the tiny graveyard, could it have been the spirit of a suicide? The girl, it is said, died tragically. What is more tragic than a person taking her own life? Or perhaps the graveyard, being a private one, was not even consecrated. Or maybe the devil took the girl's soul before she was buried.

In the meantime, the grave refuses to remain filled and, as far as we know, the unidentified ghost claws its way out of her unquiet grave each night and returns each morning.

Where she goes or who she haunts, no one knows. There have been no reports of the apparition of a young girl roaming the countryside.

Of course, all this is only supposition on my part. But the fact is that no one has dared go back to the little graveyard after dark. It's not really a fear of the supernatural. It's just that no one wants to take a chance— just in case the story is true.

Three Murderous Sisters

When mysterious lights flicker in the windows of Christiansburg Middle School, alarming memories are rekindled in this New River Valley town. Cold shivers are likely to run up and down the spines of those who have heard chilling accounts of three sinister sisters who lived there at the turn of the century. It wasn't so long ago that citizens were afraid to answer their doors at night, or even venture out after dark.

Minions of Hell tread the streets of Christiansburg after dark.

They were called the "Black Sisters" because, in life, they always dressed as if in mourning. They were described as veiled, sombre, and austere. The sisters have been accused of murder, fraud, and witchcraft. Many thought they were totally evil. The ghost lights seen in the school windows are said to be their malevolent shades, returned from the dead.

The story of the three "Black Sisters" is closely tied to Montgomery Female Academy, a shining light in Christiansburg's academic history. The Academy opened in 1852, 60 years after Christiansburg was incorporated as the county seat of Montgomery County. (The town, itself, was named for William Christian, described as a "noted Indian fighter" by self-made frontiersman, Theodore Roosevelt.

The Academy was chartered by the Montgomery Presbytery in April. A male academy already existed in town, having been established in 1849 by the same organization.

The female academy opened in a church basement, located on the corner of South Franklin and First Streets. The Rev. Nicolas Chevalier was principal.

The school grew in both size and reputation. In 1859, the Academy moved to a $12,000 building on the land where the middle school now stands.

Over the years, ownership of the Academy passed into the hands of Mrs. O.S. Polluck. When she died, around the turn of the century, the Academy—still active—was willed to her sister, Mrs. Martha Wardlaw, and to Mrs. Wardlaw's daughters, Mrs. Mary W. Snead, Mrs. Caroline Martin, and Miss Virginia Wardlaw.

Soon afterward, the trouble started.

The sisters are described in the booklet, *Reflections: Christiansburg 1792-1992*, as "perfect examples of planned manipulation. They moved people around like figures on a chess board to fit their nefarious schemes to enslave and use persons in ways to benefit themselves."

One of these "schemes" was said to be insurance fraud.

Mary Snead's 28-year-old son lived with his wife in Lynville, Tennessee. John was a bright lad whom the sisters thought would make a fine addition to the faculty of the Academy.

Caroline visited her nephew in Lynville. She tried to persuade him to return with her to Christiansburg. His wife, however, wanted no part of the move. Caroline was insistent. Finally, in desperation, John's wife called the law, and Caroline was forcibly evicted from their home.

A short time later, Caroline was back. This time she convinced John to leave his wife behind and return with her on the next train.

At that point, John became the victim of a series of "accidents."

During the trip to Christiansburg, John mysteriously fell from the train and was badly injured. Although the incident was declared accidental, the train's brakeman said John's "accident" looked like a suicide attempt. Was he, in fact, being taken to Christiansburg against his will?

Later, while teaching at the school, John was rescued from a cistern by an alert Academy caretaker, Sonny Correll. There was no explanation as to how John got into the cistern. Correll had reached the drowning man just in time to save his life. (Another suicide attempt? Or attempted murder?)

Then, weeks later, John was discovered lying in a burning bed. The mattress had been saturated with kerosene and set afire, and John was so badly burned that he died a few hours later.

It came out that John was heavily insured by his aunts, and the original beneficiary had been changed from his wife to Virginia Wardlaw. When the suspicious insurance company balked at payment, the sisters made their way through the town in an effort to get affidavits, swearing the death was accidental.

But the townspeople would have none of it. They, like the insurance company, suspected foul play.

(After a time, however, the insurance company finally made a settlement.)

In the meantime, the sisters convinced John's brother, Fletcher, to join the Academy's faculty. Fletcher didn't need as much convincing as John. He readily divorced his wife and came to Christiansburg. There he married his first cousin, Ocey.

Meanwhile, the three sisters had piled up enormous debts in town and either could not pay them or refused to pay them. Creditors and process servers lined up at their door. The sisters' behavior became even more bizarre than usual. For instance, they took to making frequent forays to the local cemetery.

One wagon driver said he was hired by the sisters to drive them to the graveyard one night—then witnessed a horrifying spectacle.

After the sisters entered the cemetery, the driver followed, undetected. There he saw them gathered around a grave, their arms reaching skyward, muttering grotesque incantations. The hack driver froze in fear.

Word of the incident spread quickly. Townspeople whispered among themselves. Were the sisters witches?

The sisters were also nocturnal. Often, knocks would sound in the middle of the night; and when the door was opened, the sisters would be there, "veiled, sombre, and austere." People were even afraid to venture on the streets after dark for fear of meeting the sisters—which they often did.

Much to the relief of the people of Christiansburg, the sisters left town one by one, and all were gone by 1908. Fletcher and Ocey Snead had also left for parts unknown. But that was not the last that Christiansburg would hear of the mysterious trio.

In 1909, they read in the newspaper that Ocey had been found dead in a bathtub, in East Orange, New Jersey.

Apparently Fletcher and Ocey had moved into the run-down East Orange house a year earlier. A janitor said they appeared happy at first—

that is, until two women in black came to live with them. Shortly after, Fletcher left.

Ocey was pregnant. Perhaps for that reason—or some unknown reason—she stayed behind. (After all, she had no reason to believe she would be harmed—at least, at first.)

Five months later, Ocey gave birth to a baby boy.

While in the hospital, Ocey told the doctor she was being starved to death and asked for his help. But she had no chance to say anything else. The sisters confronted the doctor and told him that Ocey would have nothing else to say to him. And they even went so far as to deny Ocey further medical care.

Then one day police were summoned to the house by a woman who identified herself as Virginia Wardlaw. There they found the body of Ocey Snead, drowned in a half-filled bathtub, her head under the faucet. A nearby note said Ocey had committed suicide because she was despondent over the loss of "loved ones."

When the police questioned Virginia, her answers didn't jell, and they became suspicious. Furthermore, Ocey's husband was missing— nowhere to be found. The police assumed that he wasn't dead, but had fled. They also knew he had disappeared from New Jersey at least five months before Ocey was found dead in the bathtub.

A will was then produced in which Ocey left everything to Martha Wardlaw. That made the police even more suspicious.

For years, East Orange authorities tried to bring the sisters to trial. But there was a lack of hard evidence. However, enough circumstantial evidence was finally gathered, and the sisters came to trial on January 9, 1911.

Mary Snead pleaded guilty to manslaughter. But because of her age, she was released into the custody her son who took her to his ranch in Colorado.

Virginia Wardlaw never saw the inside of the courtroom. She starved herself to death before the trial began.

Caroline Martin was sentenced to a long stretch in the New Jersey State Prison. But her behavior proved so uncontrollable that she was finally transferred to the State Hospital for the Insane, where she soon died.

Fletcher Snead was eventually discovered working as a cook in a

Canadian logging camp. He was using an assumed name. Obviously, he didn't want to be found.

The authorities determined that he apparently had nothing to do with Ocey's death. No criminal charges were ever brought against him.

Had Fletcher tried to escape his aunts—like brother John—and had he succeeded, leaving his pregnant young wife to fend for herself? Unfortunately, we'll never know the answer to that question. Fletcher is long-dead.

After her death by starvation, Virginia's body was returned to Christiansburg and buried in Sunset Cemetery. Is it her ghost that often appears as a dim light in the windows of the middle school?

And do the ghosts of the three sisters dressed in black still roam the darkened streets of Christiansburg.

There are so many unanswered questions in this horrifying story!

The night frequently holds unnamed terrors for the living. We can only hope that three of these terrors—at least in Christiansburg—are finally gone forever.

The Ghost with Half a Head

Night travelers on the road near the "Steep Place," located in Pulaski County, may meet an apparition too horrible to be adequately described in words. But as grotesque as it is, the ghost doesn't seem to be malevolent. It just wants company.

Many years ago, the ghost visited two men journeying towards Snowville, located about eight miles south of Christiansburg. They were so shaken by the experience that they never forgot the incident.

The story begins in Christiansburg. At the close of The War Between The States, a man named Little operated a store in Graysontown. As was his custom, and like many other storekeepers, he would travel north each fall to buy new goods.

Consumers, no matter what their background, are always interested in the newest fashions and newfangled gadgets. New patent medicines were becoming popular. In far-flung corners of the New River Valley, consumers were interested in the newest items in an increasingly materialistic world. Many of Little's customers even ordered merchandise from catalogs. So in order to keep as much business as possible for himself, Little kept as much new merchandise as possible on his shelves.

The day Little returned to the New River Valley, the weather was cold and icy. Stepping from the Virginia & Tennessee Railway train, he slipped and fell underneath the car while the train was pulling away from the station. Little bounced onto the tracks, and his head was split in two by the train's wheels.

Several of the men on the platform fished Little's body from the track. He had been killed instantly. The grotesqueness of his injury caused some nearby women to scream. Men became sick. Quickly, one of the men removed his coat and threw it over the mangled head.

A day later, Little's funeral was held in a little country church. Then the remains were brought to Snowville and buried at Hall's Graveyard, located about one mile east of town on the Christiansburg Road—just beyond the Steep Place.

Local people say that the Steep Place is nearly 1,000 feet of sheer rock rising up over the New River. Actually, according to New River resident Ed Moorer, it's only a few hundred feet. But it's still a formidable-looking cliff. One thing is for sure. Anyone falling over the edge would be instantly killed.

Soon after Little's burial, the stories about the ghost began.

One night Dr. Hannacker passed the cemetery. There he was joined by a walking companion—a man with half a head. After a short distance, the apparition disappeared over the rim of the Steep Place.

A short time later, the same thing happened to the Rev. Mr. Buckingham, a Methodist minister. He, too, was passing Hall's Graveyard when he was joined by a man with half a head. The apparition accompanied him for a short distance—then disappeared over the edge of the Steep Place.

No other encounters with the ghost have been recorded in recent memory. But that doesn't mean there haven't been more. Maybe others have not been so willing to talk about their experiences because they were afraid they'd be laughed at.

So there's no telling whether the ghost still lurks in Hall's Graveyard, nor whether it has accompanied other nocturnal travelers on their journey to the Steep Place. However, it would be interesting to find out if the ghost still walks.

Anyone brave enough to find out for sure?

The Museum Ghost

Is there a ghost lurking in The Wilderness Road Regional Museum, located in the historic town of Newbern? Some say there is. In fact, a child once claimed to see it—the only one to do so.

Normally the ghost makes itself known through noises and the shifting of objects. Some people get so jumpy walking through the museum that they bolt at the slightest sound.

The museum building is 100 feet long and is covered with white weatherboard. Behind the house are six old structures—or parts of structures. Three are of historical interest—an old barn (which we shall hear of later), the ruins of an outside kitchen, and a two-story log house thought to have once been slave quarters.

The main museum structure (which faces The Wilderness Road, now State Route 611) is actually two houses joined by a third structure, built at three separate times. The building has served as a private residence, a post office, a tavern, a general store, and a resort hotel.

Newbern began life in 1810 when Adam Hance laid off a town on The Wilderness Road, about 50 miles from where the ancient thoroughfare met The Great Philadelphia Wagon Road at Big Lick (Roanoke).

Hance was not a person to do things halfway. His town would last. In order to build on one of the 29 lots in his town (each being 99 feet wide by 214^1/$_2$ feet deep), he required that each house be at least one-and-one-half stories tall, built of stone or brick (or hewed log), with seams of lime or sand. Each house had to contain two glass windows, with at least twelve panes to each window. The roofs were to be covered with shingles, and solid chimneys were to be constructed of fireproof brick or stone.

(At the time, believe it or not, many fireplace chimneys were actually constructed of logs or twigs, daubed with mud. Needless to say, this created a substantial fire hazard!)

Henry Hance (son of Adam) built the first house on Lot No. 2 in 1810. This structure now comprises the east portion of the museum. The front room, with its magnificent archway, became a post office in 1812, and Henry was named as postmaster. Later he operated a tavern in the back room while he and his family—his wife Sarah and daughter Virginia—lived overhead on the second floor.

Four years later Adam himself built a weatherboard house on Lot No. 4, right next door. In 1851 the two houses were finally connected, and the structure became one long edifice.

In 1837, Sarah Hance married Jabin B. Alexander, and the couple moved to the property, which remained in the Hance and Alexander families for the next 140 years. It was purchased by The New River Historical Society in 1980.

The house was then turned into a regional museum.

Sarah Zimmerman is curator of The Wilderness Road Regional Museum. Her office is on the second floor, in the rear of the part of the building that Adam Hance built in 1816. She says she has heard mysterious noises as she works there. Furthermore, parts of her office have shifted around without help from living hands.

She believes the museum is haunted.

"I insist the ghost is alive and well," she said as she sat talking in the reception hall of the museum. "But he's mischievous, as ghosts are apt to be. I'll give you an example. When I'm finished working in the office, I'll close the file drawers before I leave. These are big, heavy, legal-sized drawers. But as soon as I step out of the office, some of them will open up again—two or three of them.

"Then I'll be working in the office and I'll hear a rustling sound in the attic. Or I'll feel a presence, but there won't be anyone there."

So far Sarah hasn't seen anything—no apparition. And even though she believes in the existence of the ghost, she's ready to offer a natural explanation for the ghostly events.

"This building vibrates," she explained. "If an 18-wheeler goes down

611 with any speed, this building vibrates enough to loosen light bulbs in the attic. I could say the ghost does that—causes the light bulbs to loosen from their sockets. But which comes first? The chicken or the egg? I like the legend and I'll go with that."

Sarah says the ghost definitely lives in the attic. The rustling sound comes from the attic. "There's an old featherbed mattress up there," she said with a smile. "Perhaps that's where the ghost sleeps."

Sarah Zimmerman tends to make light of the haunting. Others do not. In fact, people have been hearing noises in the house for years.

There are two possible explanations for the haunting. One of these involves a card game that ended in tragedy.

In the 1830s, Newbern was a stopping off place for travelers and teamsters on The Wilderness Road. After days of travel, their thirst was unquenchable and their desire for recreation insatiable. The taverns were filled with lusty men, drinking and gambling.

One especially vigorous game of chance took place inside the tavern on Lot 2. Amiability soon turned to anger when one of the players accused the other of cheating. Soon fists slashed the air, and someone pulled a knife. Before the squabble was over, one man lay sprawled on the floor, dying.

Since then, the house is said to be haunted by a restless spirit—perhaps that same man murdered in a long-ago card game.

Ed Moorer volunteers his time to The New River Historical Society by conducting tours of The Wilderness Road Regional Museum. One afternoon a week, he takes visitors through the structure, telling exciting tales of the New River Valley and the town of Newbern.

In the three years since he has lived in the New River Valley, Ed has become quite an expert on the folklore—as well as the ghost lore—of the Valley.

Two recent experiences in the museum lead him to believe something weird really does walk the building.

One day he climbed to the second floor of the museum where several of the rooms have been set up as facsimiles of early bedrooms. As he glanced at one of the beds, he saw an odd pattern in one of the blankets covering it—just like something unseen was lying on the bed.

Of course, there was nothing there.

Another time, Ed had a conversation with a young boy who claimed to have seen something terrifying in the museum.

The little boy had just sat down in a rocking chair when he saw a strange man nearby. He was a big man, dressed in old-fashioned clothing. On his head was perched a thatch of flaming red hair. And running down his side was a stream of blood!

The apparition disappeared before the eyes of the terrified youngster.

Ed questioned the child afterward, but that was all the boy remembered about his experience.

Sarah said that the house, being very old, has more than its share of creaks and groans. Indeed, while I was walking in the later portion of the house—the part built by Adam in 1816—every footfall on the boarded floor caused something to squeak. In my case, the culprit turned out to be a large wooden cabinet standing by a window. Every time I put my weight down on a certain portion of the floor, the cabinet rattled. For a person expecting to see or hear a ghost, this can be unnerving. In fact, I had to test it out several times myself before I was satisfied there was a natural explanation for what I was hearing.

This is not the first time something like this has happened.

Since Virginia Alexander had been raised in the house, she, too, knew about the restless spirit. Just after The War Between The States, when the building was used as a rooming house for those wishing to enjoy the nearby mineral springs, several maids were employed by Mrs. Alexander. All had been told about the ghost—and all believed the story.

One day Mrs. Alexander and one of the servant girls were upstairs cleaning. Suddenly they heard a noise coming from the roof of the building. Both women looked up but couldn't see a thing.

The servant girl suddenly got very excited, then collapsed. Then she became hysterical, and it was all Mrs. Alexander could do to restrain her. She thought the ghost was going to get her!

Finally, Mrs. Alexander was able to lead the servant girl down the stairs. When she got her calmed down, Mrs. Alexander walked outside and looked up. Men were there repairing the roof. No one had informed Mrs. Alexander that the work was going to be done on that day.

Ed tells a similar story concerning two tourists several years ago. They, too, had been informed that a ghost lived in the house. When they heard a sudden, unexplained noise upstairs, both skedaddled from the museum and never came back.

These two incidents are examples of how the human mind can imagine things that aren't there—like ghosts. But not all occurrences in The Wilderness Road Regional Museum can be explained away. After all, what about the young boy who saw the apparition there? And what about the heavy file cabinet drawers opening by themselves? The mussed up bed? The rustling sounds in the attic? Or even the presence that's felt in the house on occasion?

In fact, can there be more than one ghost haunting the house? Let's thicken the plot a bit.

Justice was swift and sometimes unmerciful in the early days of this country. It was not just the "shoot first and ask questions later" mentality of some law enforcement officials. Judges tended to adhere to the letter of the law rather than the spirit. Ed Moorer said at least two people were hanged across the street in the old Newbern jail. One of these executions could have yielded the second ghost.

The War Between The States had been settled on April 9, 1865, when Lee surrendered to Grant at Appomattox Courthouse in Northern Virginia. Two-and-a-half years before that, on September 22, 1962, President Lincoln had signed his "Emancipation Proclamation." By its provisions, slaves would be legally free as of January 1, 1863.

At first, Southern slaveholders thumbed their noses at Lincoln's edict. Slaves weren't really free until after the peace was signed.

Unfortunately, freedom wielded a two-edged sword. For hundreds of years, black slaves had depended on their owners to provide the necessities of life. Suddenly they were thrust out on their own. Many were confused—overwhelmed by sudden liberty.

(Many slaves didn't even have a last name. They were known as "Bill" or "Ol' Tom" or "Little Sarah." In desperation, and for legal reasons, many slaves adopted the last name of their former owners. Members of my family, for example, were slave holders on the Eastern Shore of Maryland. After the war, some of the newly-freed slaves adopted Price—a decidedly un-African name. Today, many black families named Price could probably trace their ancestry back to my family's plantation.)

After freedom, blacks could not often find work. Freedom did not mean the end of prejudice. Some stayed with their former masters. Others became sharecroppers. Invariably, starvation raised its ugly head.

In spite of the lofty principles of freedom, former slaves still suffered—even died of starvation.

A man with a large—and very hungry—family lived near Newbern. In the barn behind the Alexander house was a large stash of grain, stored in a bin. One day the former slave sneaked into the cellar of the barn and drilled a hole in the floor—right into the grain bin. As the grain funneled through the two-inch hole, the man filled a large gunnysack. Then he took it home where his wife prepared a meal for the starving family.

The man returned time and time again to the barn—each time unplugging the hole to filch another sackful of corn. And each time, he returned home to a grateful family with his bounty. There is no indication as to whether he told them where he had gotten it.

If he had taken only one sackload, the man would have probably gotten away with his theft. But he was caught and hauled before the judge.

Jabin Alexander told the court that if he had only known that the man and his family were hungry, he would have given him corn for meal and seed for planting. He probably even pleaded for the man's life. But it was too late. As I said, in those days justice was quick and uncompromising.

By law, any Negro convicted of stealing would have to be executed. There was no appeal.

And so, in 1869, this man who had stolen grain to feed his family was hanged in the old jail in Newbern for his crime.

Today the hole can still be seen in the wooden floor of the old barn—a vivid reminder of a time of human injustice based upon the color of the skin.

Does the ghost of that former slave roam the house and grounds of the old Alexander residence? He would certainly have good reason to do so!

Ed Moorer indicated that the log building (called "The Granary") could also be haunted as well.

If so, the ghosts of The Wilderness Road Regional Museum are constant reminders of a long-past day when death could be doled out for no better reason than the turn of a card or the simple "crime" of being hungry.

The Last Wish

Dessie and Boiling Breedlove lived in a two-story brick farmhouse in Blue Ridge, Virginia, located right outside Roanoke. Upstairs, there were only two bedrooms. The smaller of the two rooms was used as a bedroom for Boiling and his wife. The other bedroom was so large that it contained three complete bedroom sets.

Downstairs, a porch stretched across the entire front of the house. Inside, on the left, was the living room. On the right was a sitting room. At the rear was a kitchen.

Although Boiling Breedlove worked for Blue Ridge Stone Quarry all day long, he still found time to cultivate a large garden and tend a sty filled with hogs.

The Breedloves moved into the house in the 1940s, and some of their large family still lived with them at the time. Others were in the service, and when they came home on leave, the large upstairs bedroom was filled to capacity.

Soon after the Breedloves moved into their house, they began hearing footsteps. If the family was downstairs, footsteps could be heard overhead. The noises became so commonplace that Dessie named her ghost Flip-Flop.

One day a granddaughter was visiting the house. There was a knock on the front door. When she opened the door, no one was there. But footsteps were heard walking across the living room floor. Then the footsteps ascended the front stairs.

Curious, but not frightened, the family followed the sounds to the second floor. Again, no one was there.

A few minutes later, the clomp-clomp of footsteps resounded again, this time descending the stairs. Then the front door opened all by itself—just like someone had opened it to walk outside.

Elaine Lang married early. By the time she was 16, she was a mother with an infant son. Elaine and her child visited her grandparents regularly in Blue Ridge. Then, in 1958, her grandfather had a stroke.

Fortunately, Boiling Breedlove had a strong constitution. Each day, over the next year, his condition improved. His speech, which was slurred so badly at first, steadily improved. You had to listen to him carefully, but eventually you could make out what he was saying.

Boiling was looking forward, with much anticipation, to the coming holiday season, because his condition had improved so much. Christmas was, by far, the biggest event of the year in the big house in Blue Ridge. Dessie Breedlove had been cooking for weeks. She had baked almost every kind of cake under the sun. There were cookies and fruit salad, ham and turkey.

The whole house was gaily festooned. In the living room, greens adorned the walls.

The whole family planned to assemble at Blue Ridge on Christmas Eve. They had two reasons to celebrate this year—the season, itself, and Boiling's rapid recovery from his stroke.

That morning, for the first time in a year, Boiling Breedlove dressed himself completely. He was even able to button his shirt by himself. After lunch he sat at the kitchen table, holding his four-year-old grand-niece on his lap. He was talking about Santa Claus and the fact that the entire family would assemble that afternoon to celebrate. He was especially pleased because he was going to see his new great-granddaughter (Elaine's new baby) for the first time.

Suddenly he raised his hand to his head, as if in terrible pain, keeled over from the chair, and fell on the child. Boiling Breedlove was dead before he hit the floor.

At that very moment Elaine Lang, her husband, her mother and father, her four-year-old son, and her brand-new baby daughter were on their way from Arlington, approaching Blue Ridge.

Needless to say, Christmas was a sad day in the Breedlove household.

After the funeral, the family began to settle down into their routine once again. Elaine decided that she would remain at the house to help her grandmother.

The New Year came and went. Shortly afterward, Elaine was lying on her bed, in the small bedroom, reading. The bed had been pushed against the wall. Her infant daughter slept between Elaine and the wall.

"I was lying on my side," Elaine said, "and I suddenly felt that someone was watching me. I started to turn, and I saw the outline of a man. The only way I could describe him was that he was dark. As soon as I saw the outline, I immediately thought of my grandfather. Even though I knew that he wouldn't hurt me, I was too chicken to turn and look full force at him.

"I closed my eyes and turned the lights out. But I knew it was my grandfather, come back once again to see his great-granddaughter. He had died before we arrived.

"But I was so afraid of what I might see that I didn't open my eyes again until next morning."

Tying It All Together: Final Words

After writing two successful books of ghost tales, I'm often asked whether or not I actually believe in ghosts. I have a pat answer for that question: "I'd be mighty disappointed if there weren't no such thing."

To some people, that sounds like a cop-out, but it's what I believe. I'm a folklorist, not a ghost hunter. But that's not to say my mind is closed to the existence of the supernatural. In fact, I don't think I'm much different from thousands of other people in Southwest Virginia and Northeast Tennessee.

But, I'll go you one step further in the interest of clarification: I'd also be mighty disappointed if, one day, science proves without a shadow of a doubt that there's no such thing as a Loch Ness monster or a Sasquatch! I believe we humans need our illusions and the hope that there are still some mysteries out there that might never be solved.

It *is* important, however, that others *do* believe or, at least, care enough to perpetuate ghostlore in Southwest Virginia. And I guess that I fit into that category. That's one of the reasons I've set down some of these tales in this volume.

As can be seen by the stories in this book, Southwest Virginia is rich in ghostlore. This is only a sampling, however—24 tales out of hundreds I've collected over the past year.

Why Southwest Virginia's fascination with ghost stories and strange tales? For one thing, the attraction comes honestly and goes back hundreds of years. Scottish folklorist Barbara McDermitt once told me, "In the case of the early settlers in the mountains, their isolated life-style and lack of amenities, never mind luxuries, demanded that they be self-reliant in their work as well as entertainment, which they had to create themselves. Singing of ballads and telling the tales they brought with them from [the Old World], or heard [elsewhere], and mixed with people of many cultures, was a natural thing to do."

From her explanation, it sounds like the creation of ghost tales was almost as natural as sleeping!

People not only fear the supernatural, they are fascinated with it. Perhaps that is why the shelf of horror movies in tape rental centers is, in some establishments, larger than for comedy or children's films. Perhaps that is why one of the best-selling authors of all time is Stephen King and why Peter Straub and Anne Rice are such respected and popular storytellers. Perhaps that is why the most popular type of tale told at the National Storytelling Festival in Jonesborough is the ghost story.

"People need to have an explanation for events that are out of the ordinary," said educational psychologist Sharon Turnbull, former Director of the Center for Adult Programs and Services at East Tennessee State University. "The explanation they choose might have to do with the supernatural. Others might choose an explanation to do with science, random events, fate, or whatever. But they need to have an explanation that they can believe—one that explains what happened, one that gives them some sort of cognitive control over [the event]."

Those unfamiliar with ghost stories may choose to believe scientific explanations for every unexplained event that occurs. Others, with a penchant for the supernatural, may have other explanations. Unfortunately, some of these appear to have been bounced off the wall too many times. And too many scientific minds are quick to offer explanations about what we're really seeing when we *think* we see a ghost.

Take for example the notion that a ghost "floats" instead of "walks." Psychiatrist John Frosch of Brookdale Hospital, Brooklyn, New York, says that our perception of ghosts that float may be a "product of our childhood," since infant attention, he says, is normally focused on the face of the parent. He writes in *American Imago* magazine:

"As far as one can tell, the very young child looking at an adult in motion sees a face or head or subsequently the upper part of the body moving without the means whereby it moves. In a sense, it sees a 'floating object.' During the night time when the parent comes in to feed the child or to look in on it for one or another reason, the awakened child, in the dim light of the room, sees a blurred figure coming toward or leaving, but sees this figure moving without awareness of the means of locomotion. In a sense, it 'floats' around the room. It is this perception of hazy, blurred, nightly figures floating around which may well persist in the form of the floating ghost."

Folklorist Richard Blaustein told me that he believes that modern encounters with the supernatural are, for the most part, preconceived, and that's the reason so many of the stories sound so familiar. "The reason why we keep finding similarities between these stories," he said, "is that the previous stories that we've determined about ghosts affect the way in which we experience these things. And then we, when talking about them, fall back on motifs of ghost stories and, perhaps in some cases, [do it unconsciously]."

Recent research by popular culturist Jack Santino seems to bear out Blaustein's hypothesis. Santino, assistant professor in the Department of Popular Culture of Bowling Green University, proposed that the power of suggestion exerted an overwhelming force over logic—at least, when it came to experiencing ghostly phenomena.

Santino's research concerned the reported sightings of a ghost of a flight engineer who was killed when his plane crashed into the Florida Everglades in the early 1970s. Several years after the incident, a chronicling of the ghostly events was set down by John B. Fuller in a book entitled **The Ghost of Flight 401**.

After the tragedy, according to interviews conducted by Santino, the shade of the engineer was seen on subsequent American Airlines flights, especially on those where there was impending danger. Officials of American refused to talk about the sightings in public and forbade their employees to air their views. Privately, however, flight attendants were more than willing to share their knowledge of the ghost with Santino and to pass along experiences of others who had seen him.

In his research, Santino first attempted to prove that belief in ghosts (in this case, the flight engineer) exists among those working in the same profession as the deceased (in the same way that railroad engineers would believe in the ghost of Casey Jones). But then, Santino was startled to discover that the majority of those who told him of "personal" experiences with the ghost *confessed they had obtained most of their information from Fuller's book*!

In the *Journal of American Folklore*, Santino wrote: "We have here a case of a [close association] of folklore and written, published material. Fuller did not create the legend, although his book has clearly influenced and helped to disseminate the narratives. The flight attendants often say that Fuller's book is the source of their knowledge, while he in turn says that he learned of the ghost from flight attendants. A comparison of the lore I have collected with the published materials reveals that in many cases, a flight attendant will identify Fuller's book as the source of a story that in fact is not contained in that volume. Nevertheless, the existence of this publication acts as a validating factor when the ghost is being discussed, especially with outsiders."

Could that same association (or suggestion) be the reason that my friend saw the ghost of Vera float into her room that Halloween night? Certainly, she had spent the entire evening hearing stories about the ghost of Virginia Intermont College. Does the telling of a ghostly tale inspire realistic re-creations of more ghostly phenomena? Or, as she insists, did she really see a ghost?

No matter what stance you take on the "reality" of ghosts, there is no doubt, in my mind at least, that similar ghost stories exist in all countries and on all continents. The motifs, no matter what the source of the story, remain essentially the same. There are ghosts said to exist in Abingdon, New York, Big Stone Gap, London, Saltville, Paris, Coeburn, Tokyo, Bristol, Los Angeles, Wise, Berlin, and Christiansburg. What gives an individual story its distinctive flavor, however, is the culture from whence it sprang.

When we read in the **Epic of Gilgamesh** about the wanderings of the unquiet dead in the desert, we can equate that to the Tazewell County tale of a tragic young woman rising from the grave and walking the countryside. If we hear a Scottish folktale about the spirit of a young girl who committed suicide, we easily can think of Vera and her ghostly shenanigans at Virginia Intermont College.

Richard Blaustein said, "I would say on the surface of it, we are not going to find substantially different beliefs in the characteristics of ghosts in, say, the British Isles, and in the United States. I think, possibly, you might find some superficial differences in the ways in which ghosts are interpreted. But I think that the ghost experience is a cross-

ghosts are interpreted. But I think that the ghost experience is a cross-cultural, and possibly even a trans-cultural type of experience.

As for the ghost tales of Southwest Virginia, I believe these are the evolutionary result of stories that have existed from the beginning of history, passed orally from one generation to the other. But the real importance here is not whether ghosts actually exist, or even whether they exist in Southwest Virginia. These tales, rather, are present-day reflections of ourselves, our beliefs, our traditions, who we are, and what we are.

In this respect, the ghostly tales of Southwest Virginia are one of our most important cultural resources. As such, they should, at all cost, be preserved for future generations.